# CHILD DEVELOPMENT

## SECOND EDITION

J809

Miranda Walker

Boost

HODDER
EDUCATION
AN HACHETTE UK COMPANY

The teaching content of this resource is endorsed by OCR for use with specification OCR Level 1/Level 2 Cambridge National in Child Development (J809).

All references to assessment, including assessment preparation and practice questions of any format/style are the publisher's interpretation of the specification and are not endorsed by OCR.

This resource was designed for use with the version of the specification available at the time of publication. However, as specifications are updated over time, there may be contradictions between the resource and the specification, therefore please use the information on the latest specification and Sample Assessment Materials at all times when ensuring students are fully prepared for their assessments.

Endorsement indicates that a resource is suitable to support delivery of an OCR specification, but it does not mean that the endorsed resource is the only suitable resource to support delivery, or that it is required or necessary to achieve the qualification.

OCR recommends that teachers consider using a range of teaching and learning resources based on their own professional judgement for their students' needs. OCR has not paid for the production of this resource, nor does OCR receive any royalties from its sale. For more information about the endorsement process, please visit the OCR website.

# Acknowledgements

Every effort has been made to trace all copyright holders, but if any have been inadvertently overlooked, the Publishers will be pleased to make the necessary arrangements at the first opportunity.

Although every effort has been made to ensure that website addresses are correct at time of going to press, Hodder Education cannot be held responsible for the content of any website mentioned in this book. It is sometimes possible to find a relocated web page by typing in the address of the home page for a website in the URL window of your browser.

Hachette UK's policy is to use papers that are natural, renewable and recyclable products and made from wood grown in well-managed forests and other controlled sources. The logging and manufacturing processes are expected to conform to the environmental regulations of the country of origin.

Orders: please contact Hachette UK Distribution, Hely Hutchinson Centre, Milton Road, Didcot, Oxfordshire, OX11 7HH. Telephone: +44 (0)1235 827827. Email education@hachette.co.uk Lines are open from 9 a.m. to 5 p.m., Monday to Friday. You can also order through our website: www.hoddereducation.co.uk

ISBN: 9781398351202

First edition published in 2017
Second edition published in 2022 by Hodder Education,
An Hachette UK Company
Carmelite House
50 Victoria Embankment
London EC4Y 0DZ
www.hoddereducation.co.uk

Impression number     10 9 8 7 6 5 4 3 2

Year     2026 2025 2024 2023 2022

Cover photo © marseus - stock.adobe.com
Illustrations by Integra Software Services Ltd.
Typeset by Integra Software Services Ltd.
Produced by DZS Grafik, Printed in Bosnia & Herzegovina
A catalogue record for this title is available from the British Library.

# Contents

# Introduction

This book will help you to develop the knowledge, understanding and practical skills you need to complete your Level 1/Level 2 Cambridge National in Child Development course. As well as preparing you for your final exam and set assignments, the book will introduce you to the childcare sector. You will learn specialist childcare knowledge and skills and will have the opportunity to design a safe environment for a childcare setting as well as carry out an observation on a child and plan a suitable play activity.

Each of the chapters in this book closely follows all the topics required for each unit in the course specification, which you can find on the OCR website. To help with your learning, the book covers the key content in detail and includes a range of real-world examples. There are also lots of activities and learning features; you can find out more about these and how to use them on page vi.

Note for teachers: You can find out more about how we have designed the textbook to support you at: www.hoddereducation.co.uk/cambridge-national-child-development

## Assessment: Examined unit and final set assignments

The Cambridge National in Child Development qualification is made up of three different units. All students will need to complete Unit R057 (Health and well-being for child development), Unit R058 (Create a safe environment and understand the nutritional needs of children from birth to five years) and Unit R059 (Understand the development of a child from one to five years).

- **Unit R057** is an examined unit where you will sit a one hour 15-minute examination paper, which is set and marked by OCR.
- **Units R058 and R059** are assessed through a series of tasks for a set assignment that you will be given. The assignments are set by OCR, marked by your tutor and then moderated by OCR.

All the examination questions contain 'command' words. These tell you what you have to do to answer a question or complete the task. A full list of common command words is available on the OCR website. Always check the command word before starting a task or answering a question. For example, if you describe something when an explanation is required, you will not be able to gain full marks; this is because an explanation requires more detail than a description. There are a range of practice questions in this book in Unit R057 to help you get to grips with the command words.

Once you have learned all the required parts of the moderated units, you will complete an assignment that will be used to assess your knowledge and skills of the subject. It will be set in a vocational context, which means that it will simulate what it would be like to be given a project by a client or employer in a work situation. You will use the OCR set assignment for the assessment. This assignment will include a series of tasks that follow the same process and sequence of the units for R058 (Create a safe environment and understand the nutritional needs of children from birth to five years) and R059 (Understand the development of a child from one to five years). The assignment practice features in this book in Units R058-R059 will help you get used to working using a childcare context.

Note: The practice questions and accompanying marks and mark schemes included in this resource are an opportunity to practice exam skills, but they do not replicate examination papers and are not endorsed by OCR.

## Plagiarism and referencing

Your work for the OCR set assignments in Units R058-R059 must be in your own words. You must not plagiarise. Plagiarism is the submission of another's work as one's own and/or failure to acknowledge the source correctly.

Sometimes you might need to use a diagram or include a quotation from someone else or a website. If you do this it is very important that you always provide a reference for any information you use that is not your own work. Quotation marks should be placed around any quoted text. You should put the source reference next to the information used. In addition to referencing the picture, diagram, table or quotation, you should explain in your own words why you have used it, what it tells you, how it relates to your work, or summarise what it means. Providing a reference means that you will include details of the source, which is where you found the information. You should include the full website address (URL) and date that you found it or, for a textbook, the page number, title, author's name, date it was published and the name of the publisher. For newspaper or magazine articles you should give the date of publication, title of the paper or magazine and the name of the author. When producing your work for the assessment, you should never use any templates or writing frames. You must always decide yourself how to present your information.

# How to use this book

## Key features of the book

The book is organised by the units in the qualification. Each unit is broken down into the topic areas from the specification. Each unit opener will help you to understand what is covered in the unit, the list of topic areas covered, and what you will be assessed on, fully matched to the requirements of the specification.

### Topic areas

The topic areas are clearly stated so you know exactly what is covered.

### How will I be assessed?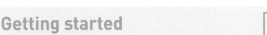

Assessment criteria are clearly listed and fully mapped to the specification.

### Getting started

Short activities to introduce you to the topic.

### Key term

Definitions of important **terms**.

### Case study

See how concepts are applied in settings and learn about real-life scenarios.

### Stretch activity

Further activities designed to test you and provide you with more in-depth knowledge and understanding of the topic.

### Test your knowledge

Questions and quick tasks to test your knowledge and understanding. Answers are provided online at: **hoddereducation.co.uk/cambridge-nationals-2022/answers**

### Activity

A short task to help you understand an idea or assessment criteria.

### Research

Activities that draw on the content covered in the book to reinforce your understanding.

### Good practice

Useful advice for when you are working with children. You don't need to know this content for your exam.

### Synoptic links

Links to relevant details in other parts of the book so you can see how topics link together.

### Read about it

Includes references to books, websites and other sources for further reading and research.

### Practice questions

This feature appears in Unit R057 where you will be assessed via an exam. Mark schemes and example answers are provided online at: **hoddereducation.co.uk/cambridge-nationals-2022/answers**

### Assignment practice

This feature appears in Units R058 and R059 and will help you prepare for non-examined assessment with model assignments. Mark schemes and example answers are provided online at: **hoddereducation.co.uk/cambridge-nationals-2022/answers**

# Health and well-being for child development

## About this unit

In this unit you will learn about the importance of being healthy before and during pregnancy, and creating conditions in which a child can thrive. You will also learn how to prevent and manage childhood illnesses, and how to create a safe environment. Understanding these key factors will enable you to help and support those in your care.

## Topic areas

In this unit you will learn about:

1  Pre-conception health and reproduction
2  Antenatal care and preparation for birth
3  Postnatal checks, postnatal care and the conditions for development
4  Childhood illnesses and a child-safe environment

Working as a health or childcare professional needs an understanding of the care needs for children of all ages, starting right from the pre-conception stage. It's important to understand the key factors that impact on becoming pregnant, having a healthy pregnancy and creating a safe and healthy environment for the baby when it is born, so that you can help and support those in your care.

## How will I be assessed?

You will take an exam covering the four topic areas of this unit:

Refer to the tables in the qualification specification to find out more about the aims for each topic area. The first column sets out the teaching content. In the exam, a direct question may be asked about any of this content. The second column shows the breadth and depth of teaching needed and indicates the range of knowledge and understanding that may be assessed in the exam.

### Knowledge and understanding

The exam will test your knowledge and understanding.

- You will need to *understand* all of the content unless the breadth and depth column identifies it as knowledge only.
- Any content that you should *know* only will start with the word 'know' in the breadth and depth column.

## Topic area 1 Pre-conception health and reproduction

## Getting started

Think of the important factors that might impact on a woman's health before she conceives. In pairs, compare and discuss your lists. If your partner has a suggestion you have overlooked, add it to your own list for future reference.

Before deciding to have children, a couple will want to be sure that they are ready. Considering their pre-conception health has an important part to play. To ensure that they do not conceive before they are ready, and to know what to expect when they do try to conceive, couples also need a good understanding of reproduction and contraception.

# 1.1 Factors affecting pre-conception health for women and men

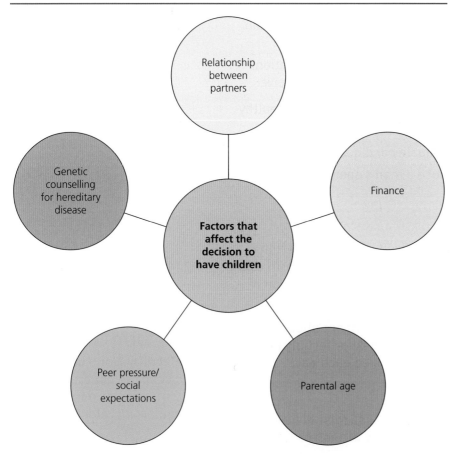

**Figure 1.1** Factors that affect pre-conception health for women and men. Why do you think it is important for men and women to be aware of these?

Every woman who could get pregnant is advised to think about her health even if she isn't currently planning a pregnancy. There are many reasons for this:

- Health can impact on levels of **fertility**. This is the case for both female and male fertility.
- Health can impact on risks to the pregnant mother and the baby.
- Around 50 per cent of pregnancies are not planned. Unplanned pregnancies are at greater risk of preterm birth and low birthweight babies.
- Around 1 in 8 babies are born too early.

Before trying to conceive a baby, women and men can take action to help prevent fertility problems. Women can also prevent some later problems by taking action on health issues and risks in advance of pregnancy.

## Key term

**Fertility** Being able to conceive children.

## Research

Using the internet, research:

- the definition of 'primary infertility'
- the definition of 'secondary infertility'
- how many couples in the UK experience fertility difficulties.

## Weight

Being a healthy weight helps to safeguard both a mother and her baby.

- In women, being overweight or obese can affect ovulation, which can in turn affect fertility and make it harder to conceive. It can also make fertility treatment less likely to work.
- However, being underweight can affect periods and ovulation, which can both affect fertility and make it harder to conceive.

For men, eating a healthy, balanced diet and maintaining a healthy weight is essential to keep sperm in good condition.

- Being overweight may affect the quality and quantity of sperm.
- Being underweight can also reduce a man's sperm quality and therefore his fertility.

## Smoking

Smoking can make conception more difficult. A woman's fertility can be affected, and men who smoke may have a lower sperm count than non-smokers. They may also produce a higher proportion of abnormal sperm.

**Infertility** rates in both male and female smokers are about twice the rate of infertility found in non-smokers. The risk for fertility problems increases with the number of cigarettes smoked each day.

## Drinking alcohol

Drinking excessive amounts of alcohol can cause men to have lower sperm counts, and it can also affect the quality of sperm.

There is also a direct link between alcohol and fertility in women. Although research is ongoing into exactly why this is, many studies have shown that even drinking lightly can have an effect.

There has also been much debate over how much alcohol is safe for a mother to drink during pregnancy. But from research it is clear that the more a woman drinks, the higher the risk to her baby. The Chief Medical Officers (CMO) for the UK recommend that if a woman is pregnant, or planning to become pregnant, the safest approach is not to drink alcohol at all.

## Taking recreational drugs

Recreational drug use can affect fertility in both men and women. If taken over a long period of time, recreational drugs can cause permanent problems with the reproductive system and infertility. Many recreational drugs can cause these issues, including:

- cannabis
- anabolic steroids
- ecstasy
- cocaine
- heroin.

> ### Key term
> **Infertility** Not being able to conceive children after 12 months (or more) of regular unprotected sex.

**Figure 1.2** It is recommended that women should not drink alcohol during pregnancy

The specific effects of recreational drugs differ, but sperm quality and quantity can be damaged in men, and hormonal production, ovulation and menstrual cycles may become erratic in women.

Very serious damage can be caused to an unborn child by smoking (including passive smoking), drinking alcohol and using recreational drugs in pregnancy. It is extremely important to protect a foetus from these factors throughout its development in the womb.

## Parental age

The age of the couple can affect the likelihood of conception.

### Age of the mother

As a woman ages, her ability to conceive and the quality of her eggs begin to decline. This decline becomes more rapid after the age of 35.

The National Health Service (NHS) reports that around one-third of couples in which the woman is over 35 have fertility problems. This rises to two-thirds when the woman is over 40. When a woman stops having a reproductive cycle (known as menopause), she will no longer be able to get pregnant.

In recent years, figures have shown more mothers are waiting to have their first child until the ages of between 35 and 45 years. This might be because women are settling down or getting married later in life than earlier generations, or they may be waiting until they are financially secure. They might have been building a career, gaining qualifications and/or training for work.

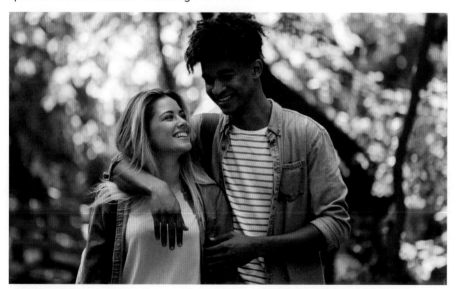

**Figure 1.3** The age of the couple can affect the likelihood of conception

### Age of the father

Men produce sperm all their adult life, including into old age. As long as they are physically capable of sexual intercourse, men can father children.

**Test your knowledge**

1 List all the factors that can contribute to fertility problems in women.

Parental age can increase the chances of a baby being born prematurely. It has also been linked to increased chances of a baby being born with certain neurological conditions.

## 1.2 Other factors affecting the pre-conception health for women

### Folic acid

Taking folic acid during pregnancy can help prevent birth defects known as neural tube defects. This includes spina bifida, a condition where a baby's spine and spinal cord do not develop properly.

Women who could become pregnant or who are planning a pregnancy are advised to take 400 micrograms (mcg) of folic acid per day as a supplement before conception and until the 12th week of pregnancy. They should also eat folate-rich foods such as green vegetables, brown rice and fortified breakfast cereals, to consume a combined total of 6000 mcg of folate a day from folate-rich foods and a supplement.

### Up-to-date immunisations

Keeping immunisations up to date will contribute to keeping a woman healthy both before and during pregnancy. This in turn benefits the baby.

## 1.3 Types of contraception methods and their advantages and disadvantages

There are many factors to consider for any couple when it comes to choosing an appropriate method of contraception. There are a range of options available that will suit a couple's preferences and needs.

### Barrier methods

The term **barrier method** means that a device is used to prevent semen (containing sperm) from passing through the cervix and coming into contact with the egg, so that this prevents conception. Barrier prevention methods are:

- male and female condoms
- diaphragm or cap.

### *Male and female condoms*

A male condom is a sheath made from latex. Polyurethane condoms are also available for those with a latex sensitivity or allergy. It is put onto the erect penis before it comes into contact with the vagina, which does mean interrupting sex in order to put one on.

---

**Test your knowledge**

1 Write down the reasons why women should take a folic acid supplement before conception and up to week 12 of their pregnancy.

---

**Key term**

**Barrier method** A method of contraception in which a device or preparation prevents sperm from reaching an egg.

A condom is 98 per cent effective if used correctly, and it also helps to protect against many sexually transmitted infections (STIs). If used incorrectly, however, a condom can come off or split open, making it ineffective.

Condoms are widely available from chemists, supermarkets, pubs, clubs and garages. They are also provided free by family planning clinics. They must be discarded after one use. An advantage of condoms is that they allow the man to take responsibility for contraception.

A female condom is a sheath made from polyurethane. It is put inside the vagina before it comes into contact with the penis, again meaning that sex is interrupted in order to put one in.

It is 95 per cent effective if used correctly, and it also helps to protect against many STIs. A disadvantage is that it is possible for the condom to be pushed too far into the vagina.

Female condoms are widely available in chemists and supermarkets, but they are more expensive than male condoms. They are often free from family planning clinics.

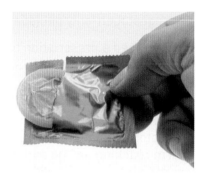

**Figure 1.4** Condoms are barrier prevention methods

Some contraceptive methods are not compatible with use immediately after giving birth or when breastfeeding, but male and female condoms can be used at any time following a birth.

## Diaphragm or cap

This is a dome-shaped piece of latex or silicone that covers the cervix. It is inserted into the vagina before sex, and must be used with spermicidal gel or cream, which will kill sperm. It can be inserted a few hours in advance, so it need not interrupt the enjoyment of sex. It is reusable, so must be removed and washed after intercourse.

The cap is 92 per cent effective if used correctly, and helps to protect against some STIs. A disadvantage is diaphragms and caps can be difficult to use, and they can cause cystitis.

If a woman has had a baby, these methods can be used again from around six weeks after giving birth. If a woman used a diaphragm or cap before becoming pregnant, she will need to see a doctor or nurse at a contraception clinic or her GP surgery after the birth, to make sure it still fits correctly. She may need a different size.

## Hormonal methods

**Hormonal methods** of contraception are available free on the NHS, and are usually prescribed following a discussion with a GP.

### Contraceptive pills

The contraceptive pill is a hormonal method of contraception, and comes in two forms:

- combined pill
- progestogen-only pill (sometimes referred to as the 'mini pill').

Women need a prescription to access the contraceptive pill, which is available for free on the NHS.

### Combined pill

The combined pill is a tablet containing hormones (oestrogen and progestogen) that prevent ovulation and so reduce the likelihood of sperm reaching an egg and of the egg becoming implanted in the womb lining.

The woman takes the pill for 21 days, then has a break for seven days, in which time she will have a period. She then starts to take the pill for another 21 days, and so on.

The pill needs to be taken regularly at the same time of day. It is 99 per cent effective if used correctly, but a woman can still become pregnant if she forgets to take it, vomits after taking it or has severe diarrhoea.

While it can help women with heavy/painful periods and may help to protect against cancer of the womb, ovaries and colon, the combined pill can also cause side effects such as weight gain, headaches, mood swings or depression, raised blood pressure and, uncommonly, blood clots. Using this method does not interrupt sex.

If a woman is breastfeeding, has certain health conditions or is at risk of blood clots, they are generally advised not to take the combined contraceptive pill until at least six weeks after birth. If these factors do not apply, it is usually fine to take the combined pill from three weeks after giving birth.

### Progestogen-only pill

This pill contains the progestogen hormone only. It is taken every day, and this needs to be done within a specified three-hour period.

This kind of pill works by causing the mucus in the cervix to thicken so that sperm cannot come into contact with an egg. It also thins the womb lining, stopping a fertilised egg from becoming implanted. (Some women actually stop ovulating altogether when taking this pill.)

**Key term**

**Hormonal method** A method of contraception in which hormones prevent eggs from being released from the ovaries, thicken cervical mucus to prevent sperm from entering the uterus, and thin the lining of the uterus to prevent implantation.

This pill is 99 per cent effective if used correctly, but a woman can still become pregnant if she forgets to take it, vomits after taking it, has severe diarrhoea or takes certain medication. Women who cannot take oestrogen may be able to take this pill.

Side effects can include spot-prone skin and tender breasts, and periods may be irregular. Using this method does not interrupt sex. This method can be used immediately after giving birth.

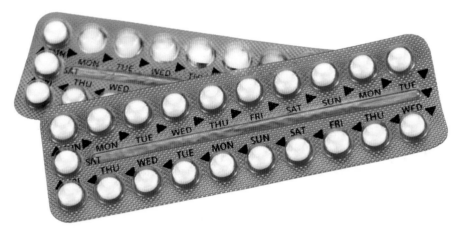

**Figure 1.5** The contraceptive pill is a hormonal method of contraception

## Contraceptive injection

A woman receives an injection every few weeks – the most common type is given every 12 weeks by a health professional. This might be a suitable choice for women who find it difficult to take a tablet at the same time each day.

This method works by causing the mucus in the cervix to thicken so that sperm cannot come into contact with an egg. It also thins the womb lining, stopping a fertilised egg from becoming implanted. (Some women actually stop ovulating altogether.) It is 99 per cent effective if used correctly, and can protect against some cancers and infections.

Side effects can include headaches, tender breasts, weight gain and mood swings, and there may be irregular periods.

After stopping the injections, it can take up to a year to get fertility levels back to normal, so this is not a good choice for those planning a pregnancy in the near future. Using this method does not interrupt sex. This method can be used immediately after giving birth.

## Contraceptive implant

A health professional will insert this small flexible tube into the skin of a woman's upper arm. It releases the progestogen hormone into the body to stop the ovaries from releasing an egg and thickens the mucus in the cervix, preventing sperm from reaching an egg. It also makes the womb less likely to accept a fertilised egg.

The implant is 99 per cent effective if used correctly. It is removed after three years, therefore the couple do not need to think about contraception during this time. Some medicines may make it ineffective, however.

Possible side effects include swelling, tenderness or bruising after it is inserted, and periods may change to become lighter, or heavier and longer. It does not protect against STIs. This method can be used immediately after giving birth.

### Intrauterine device/system

An intrauterine device or system (IUD or IUS), also referred to as the coil, is a small, T-shaped plastic device that is inserted into the uterus by a doctor or nurse. It releases the progestogen hormone into the womb, which thickens the mucus in the cervix, preventing sperm from reaching an egg. It also thins the womb lining so that a fertilised egg is less likely to be implanted. (Some women actually stop ovulating altogether.)

**Figure 1.6** An IUD or IUS is a device that sits inside the uterus

This contraception is 99 per cent effective if used correctly for five years or three years, depending on the type, therefore the couple do not need to think about contraception during this time.

It may make periods lighter, shorter or stop altogether, so it can help women who have heavy or painful periods. It can also be used by women who cannot take the combined pill.

Possible side effects include mood swings, skin problems, breast tenderness and getting an infection after it is inserted. Insertion can also be uncomfortable. It does not protect against STIs.

This method can be used immediately after giving birth. However, if an IUD or IUS is not inserted within 48 hours of the birth, women will usually be advised to wait until four weeks after the birth.

Also available is a copper IUD, which is also 99 per cent effective. The copper, rather than a hormone, stops the sperm moving through the womb towards the egg. In the first six months of use, it is common to have spotting and light bleeding between periods, and heavier or prolonged bleeding and pain.

### Contraceptive patch

This patch is worn on the skin and introduces hormones to the body (oestrogen and progestogen).

- It works by causing the mucus in the cervix to thicken so that sperm cannot come into contact with an egg.
- It also thins the womb lining, stopping a fertilised egg from becoming implanted.

It is 99 per cent effective if used correctly and may protect against some cancers and infections. It is still effective if the woman vomits or has severe diarrhoea (unlike the pill).

Side effects can include headaches and raised blood pressure, and, uncommonly, blood clots. The patch must be changed each week for three weeks, then there is a week off.

Using this method does not interrupt sex.

### Emergency contraceptive pill

This is designed to prevent pregnancy after a woman has had unprotected sex, or if she thinks that the method of conception has failed – a condom may have split, for instance. The sooner a woman takes an emergency contraceptive pill after unprotected sex, the more effective it will be. But it must be taken within either 72 hours (three days) or 120 hours (five days).

The emergency pill can be bought from a pharmacy (by those aged 16 and over) and is also available free of charge from some GP surgeries, family planning and sexual health clinics, NHS walk-in centres and hospitals.

There are two types of emergency contraceptive pill.

- Levonelle: This must be taken within 72 hours (3 days) of unprotected sex. It is more effective if taken as soon as possible after unprotected sex. It is thought to prevent up to 95 per cent of pregnancies if taken within 24 hours, up to 85 per cent if taken within 25–48 hours and up to 58 per cent if taken within 49–72 hours.

  Levonelle is safe to take when breastfeeding. Small amounts of the pill's hormones may pass into the breast milk, but it is not thought to be harmful to babies.
- ellaOne: This must be taken within five days (120 hours) of unprotected sex – allowing an extra 48 hours over Levonelle. ellaOne is thought to remain up to 98 per cent effective throughout the five-day window. It is not recommended for use more than once in one menstrual cycle.

  The safety of this pill during breastfeeding is not yet known. The manufacturer recommends that women do not breastfeed for one week after taking the pill.

## Natural family planning

In this process, a woman records the symptoms in her body that indicate when she is fertile and able to conceive. This includes:

- the temperature method: monitoring her temperature
- the cervical mucus method: monitoring bodily secretions
- the calendar method: monitoring the dates in her menstrual cycle.

A woman may monitor all of these and might use a diary or app to help her track observations. This method requires rigorous tracking and monitoring to be accurate.

A woman will be fertile and able to conceive for a period of around eight days in each month. On other days, she will be able to have sex without conceiving.

On the fertile days, a condom can be used if the couple wish to have sex, or they can abstain (not have sex). This means that the method is compatible with all cultures and faiths (because some do not permit the use of contraception).

This form of contraception is up to 98 per cent effective if used correctly, but it can take time to learn to identify the fertile days, and it does not offer protection against STIs. There are no side effects or costs, and it can be used when breastfeeding.

**Figure 1.7** Using a calendar to track symptoms

## Activity

Imagine that you have been asked to make a poster that informs young adults of the important factors to consider when choosing a method of contraception (e.g. effectiveness and protection against STIs).

- Decide what factors the poster will incorporate.
- Decide what information will be given about each factor.
- Design the poster.

## Test your knowledge

1 Outline the choices available for couples who want to use barrier methods of contraception.
2 What is the main difference between the functions of the contraceptive pill and the emergency contraceptive pill?

# 1.4 The structure and function of the reproductive systems

To understand how reproduction happens, you first need to understand the structure and function of the male and female reproductive systems.

## The female reproductive system

The female reproductive system includes the:

- ovaries
- Fallopian tubes
- uterus/womb
- cervix
- vagina
- the menstrual cycle.

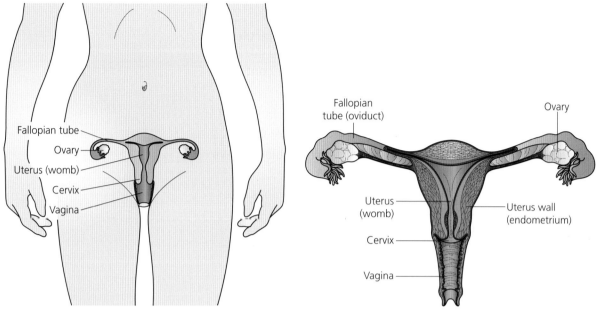

**Figure 1.8** Female reproductive system

## Ovaries

A woman's two ovaries control the production of the hormones oestrogen and progesterone, which govern the development of the female body and the menstrual cycle. Inside the ovaries are undeveloped egg cells called ova (one cell is called an ovum).

## Fallopian tubes

These tubes connect the ovaries to the uterus and are lined by minute hairs called cilia. Each month, one of the ovaries releases an egg into a tube, and the hairs help the egg to reach the uterus by wafting it along the tube.

## Uterus/womb

The uterus (also called the womb) is the hollow, pear-shaped muscular bag where the foetus grows and develops. The lining of the uterus is soft, and it is here that an egg will become implanted.

## Cervix

This is a very strong ring of muscles between the uterus and vagina, and it is usually closed. It keeps the foetus securely in place in the womb throughout pregnancy. The cervix dilates (opens) during labour to allow the baby to be born.

## Vagina

This muscular tube leads downwards, connecting the cervix to the outside of the body. It is here that the man's penis enters the body during sex. Folds of skin called labia meet at the entrance of the vagina, forming the vulva. Urine passes through the urethra, which opens into the vulva but is separate from the vagina.

## The menstrual cycle

This is the cycle in which women have their periods and are fertile (can conceive). Girls begin having periods when they become sexually mature (the average age for periods starting is 12) and they continue until menopause (the average age for this is 51).

- Women experience periods differently, but menstruation (a period) generally lasts three to seven days, with an average of five days.
- A period signals the start of the menstrual cycle, when blood flows from the uterus and leaves the body via the vagina.
- A new egg then develops in one of the ovaries. About 14 days after the first day of menstruation, the egg is released from the ovary and travels along the Fallopian tube to the uterus.
- The lining of the uterus will be thickened and ready for an egg to be fertilised by sperm. If this occurs, a foetus will start to grow.
- If fertilisation does not occur by the end of the cycle, the blood, uterus lining and egg are flushed out via another period and the cycle begins again.

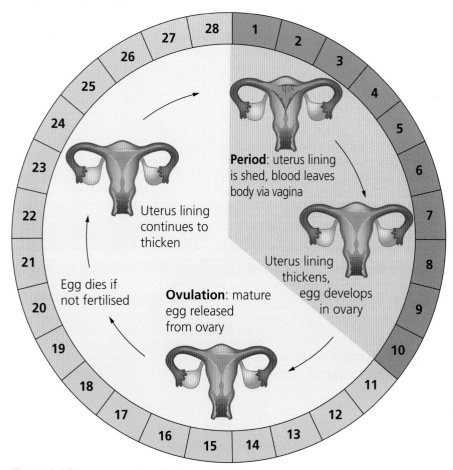

**Figure 1.9** The menstrual cycle diagram

## Male reproductive system

The male reproductive system includes the:

- testes
- sperm duct system/epididymis
- urethra
- penis
  - vas deferens
  - seminal vesicle.

### Testes

The scrotum is a bag of skin that contains two testes. These make millions of sperm – the male sex cells. They also produce hormones including testosterone, which governs the development of the male body.

### Sperm duct system/epididymis

The sperm duct system consists of the epididymis, which contains the sperm, and the vas deferens, which are the sperm ducts (tubes) that sperm pass through.

Glands produce nutrient-rich fluid – called semen – which mixes with the sperm and carries it.

### Urethra

This tube inside the penis carries both urine and semen, but not both at the same time. A ring of muscle controls this.

### Penis

The penis consists of the shaft (the main part that goes inside the vagina) and the glans (the tip), which has a small opening. Through this opening, sperm and urine leave the body (separately) via the urethra.

- Vas deferens: This is a muscular tube that extends upwards from the testicles, transferring sperm that contains semen to the urethra.
- Seminal vesicles: The seminal vesicles are a pair of glands found in the male pelvis. The glands produce many of the ingredients of semen, providing around 70 per cent of the total volume of semen. During ejaculation, the smooth muscle layer of the seminal vesicles contracts, releasing the seminal vesicle fluid.

# 1.5 How reproduction takes place

There is a point in the menstrual cycle which either ends with conception and reproduction (a baby being born), or with the woman's body flushing out an unfertilised egg.

## Ovulation

This occurs when an egg is released from one of the ovaries and travels along the Fallopian tube, around day 14 of the menstrual cycle. It is moved along by the cilia, and a jelly-like coating stops it from sticking to the sides of the tubes.

## Conception/fertilisation

This occurs when a sperm penetrates an egg following ejaculation of sperm from the penis into the vagina. The sperm passes through the cervix and uterus, meets the egg in the Fallopian tube and loses its tail, which is no longer needed.

The egg and sperm then fuse as one cell. The fertilised egg continues along the Fallopian tube. Between four and five days later, there is a mass of around 16 cells. This forms a ball of tissue (the blastocyst).

## Implantation

After around another seven days, the fertilised egg arrives in the uterus and implants itself in the enriched lining. Once it is attached firmly, conception has been achieved and the egg is called an embryo.

## Development of the embryo and foetus

The outer cells of the embryo link with the mother's blood supply, forming the baby's support system – the umbilical cord, amnion and placenta (the baby will receive nutrients through the placenta from the mother).

### Amniotic fluid

The amniotic fluid is the protective liquid which is contained in an amniotic sac. This provides a cushion for the foetus, helping to keep it safe from bumps and injury. It also contains nutrients, hormones and antibodies which are important for the baby.

At first, the fluid consists of water from the mother's body. As the foetus grows, it is also made up of the baby's urine.

### Umbilical cord

The umbilical cord is a tube that connects the foetus to the mother during pregnancy. It has a vein that takes food and oxygen from the placenta to the baby, and two arteries that carry waste from the baby to the placenta.

## Placenta

The placenta is an organ that develops in the mother's uterus during pregnancy. It is attached to the wall of the uterus. The baby's umbilical cord arises from the placenta. The placenta supplies oxygen and nutrients to the baby and removes waste products from the baby's blood.

## How the embryo becomes a foetus

At the age of eight weeks, the embryo becomes a foetus. At this point, the foetus is generally about 1 inch long and weighs around $\frac{1}{30}$ of an ounce. The development of the embryo is shown in Figure 1.10 – study this carefully.

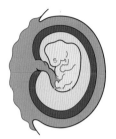

Embryo 6–7 weeks

**Figure 1.10** Development of the embryo

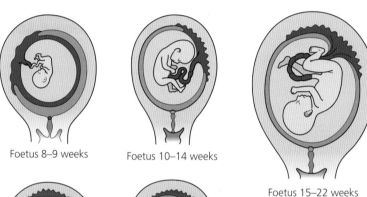

Foetus 8–9 weeks          Foetus 10–14 weeks

Foetus 15–22 weeks

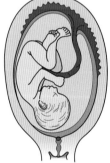
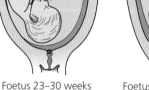

Foetus 23–30 weeks          Foetus 31–40 weeks

**Figure 1.11** Development of the foetus

The development of the foetus is shown in Figure 1.11 – study this carefully as well.

## Multiple pregnancies

A multiple pregnancy is when more than one baby grows in the uterus. There are different types of multiple pregnancies:

- Identical twins: one fertilised egg divides into two cells.
- Non-identical/fraternal twins: two separate eggs are released and fertilised by two different sperm.

**Activity**

Discuss the following with a partner:

- At what age do you think the foetus looks human, and is fully formed in miniature?
- At what age do you think the foetus can be felt by the pregnant mother?
- At what age do you think the baby could realistically be expected to survive if born early? (This is known as the age at which a baby is 'legally viable'.)

## 1.6 The signs and symptoms of pregnancy

There are some common signs and symptoms of pregnancy, but not all women will have all of the symptoms. Women also experience signs and symptoms at different rates – this means that some women are further along in the pregnancy than others when they find out that they are pregnant.

### Breast changes

The breasts may feel similar to just before a period, becoming larger and feeling tender. Some women may feel tingling and veins may be more visible. The nipples may appear darker and stand out.

### Missed period

The first sign of pregnancy is often a missed period, or a very light period. This is generally the most reliable sign for women who usually have a regular monthly menstrual cycle.

### Nausea

Feeling sick and nauseous, and/or vomiting when pregnant, is often called 'morning sickness', although it can occur at any time of day. This symptom generally begins around six weeks after a pregnant woman's last period.

### Passing urine frequently

Pregnant women often need to pass urine more frequently. There may also be constipation and an increase of vaginal discharge without any soreness or irritation.

### Tiredness

Women may feel tired or exhausted, particularly during the first 12 weeks of pregnancy, because of hormonal changes in the body. These hormonal changes can also cause a woman to feel emotional and upset at this time.

**Figure 1.12** Women experience different signs and symptoms of pregnancy

---

### Practice question ✔

Daniel and Melanie are considering their contraceptive options.

State the different types of barrier methods available to them.

[3 marks]

---

### Test your knowledge ✔

1 What is the function of a woman's ovaries in reproduction?
2 What happens at the implantation stage of conception?

## Topic area 2 Antenatal care and preparation for birth

## 2.1 The purpose and importance of antenatal clinics

### The meaning of the term antenatal

**Antenatal care** is the care given to a pregnant mother and her unborn baby during pregnancy and ahead of the birth. Some aspects of antenatal care also extend to the father or the mother's partner.

Antenatal clinics provide antenatal care. Through regular appointments, these clinics prepare the mother for a safe pregnancy and delivery by:

- carrying out routine tests/checks
- carrying out screening and diagnostic checks
- providing antenatal (parenting) classes.

### The timing of the first antenatal clinic appointment

The first antenatal clinic appointment should take place before week 10 of a pregnancy and may happen from week 8. The majority of first appointments occur between weeks 8–12. Some women may not know they are pregnant by week 8, or may not have visited their GP yet.

### The roles of the different health professionals

A pregnant mother will be supported by a team of health professionals.

### *General practitioner*

The GP is generally a mother's first port of call following a positive home pregnancy test.

The GP will confirm the pregnancy and book the mother into the 'maternity system' so that specific appointments for scans and check-ups are set up. Some mothers will receive news of their pregnancy from the GP after presenting with signs of pregnancy at the doctor's surgery. The GP's role also includes:

- answering any initial questions the pregnant mother may have
- discussing any specific issues they think may be relevant to the pregnancy, for example, a mother's existing medical conditions, and making referrals to other professionals as necessary

**Key term**

**Antenatal care** The care given to a pregnant mother and her unborn baby during pregnancy and ahead of the birth.

**Figure 1.13** Professionals supporting the pregnant mother

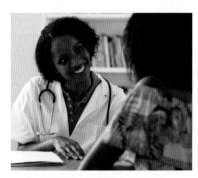

**Figure 1.14** A GP can be a first port of call for new mothers

- treating the mother for any non-pregnancy related medical problems during pregnancy
- responding to emergency concerns relating to the pregnancy – for example, they may be called out to visit a mother experiencing abdominal pain
- potentially being involved in the delivery of babies in GP-led units (see section 2.4)
- providing postnatal medical care, including giving advice on matters such as contraception following the birth.

## Midwife

The word 'midwife' literally means 'with woman'.

Midwives are experts in normal pregnancy and birth (vaginal birth without the need of interventions). They look after a pregnant woman and her baby throughout the phase of antenatal care, during labour and birth, and for up to 28 days after the baby has been born.

The responsibilities of midwives include:

- providing full antenatal care, including parenting classes, clinical examinations and screening
- identifying high-risk pregnancies
- monitoring women and supporting them during labour and the birthing process
- teaching new and expectant mothers how to feed, care for and bathe their babies.

**Figure 1.15** Midwives take care of the pregnant woman and her baby

Midwives fall into three categories:

1 Hospital midwives: These midwives are based in a hospital, a birth centre or midwife-led unit. They also work in antenatal clinics, and on the labour and postnatal wards.

2 Community midwives: These midwives see pregnant women at home or at a specialised clinic. (Clinics may also be found within children's centres and GP surgeries.) They also attend home births, and are responsible for the provision of postnatal care for both home births and hospital births. They will visit new mothers at home after the birth for up to ten days. Midwifery services are increasingly moving from hospitals to the community.

3 Independent midwives: These midwives work privately, outside the NHS. They are most likely to work with women intending to have a home birth.

**Activity**

With a partner, think of a sentence that defines the role of a midwife. This should begin 'A midwife's role is to …'.

**Research**

Carry out an internet search on midwife services in your area. Which types of midwife support mothers locally?

## *Obstetrician*

Midwives take on the antenatal care of mothers considered at low risk, and the supervision of uncomplicated deliveries that will not require medical intervention. More complex cases are taken on by an obstetrician.

This can be in response to:

- a pre-existing acute or chronic medical condition in the mother that complicates the pregnancy and/or birth
- a complication with the mother or baby identified during pregnancy that complicates the pregnancy and/or birth
- a baby becoming distressed during labour.

An obstetrician's role includes assisting delivery and performing **Caesarean sections**.

## The reasons for routine tests/checks and what conditions they can identify

At weeks 8–12 of the pregnancy, a mother will have her first antenatal appointment, usually with a midwife. During the appointment, the midwife will carry out some routine checks (see below). These checks will be repeated on later visits, to monitor the health of mother and baby.

The midwife will ask lots of questions to build up a picture of the mother's medical history, and will organise an appointment for the first scan.

### *Baby's heartbeat*

The baby's heartbeat will be checked and monitored at each appointment. This confirms that the baby is alive.

The midwife will also be listening to hear if the heartbeat is normal. The expected heartbeat of an unborn baby is 110–160 beats per minute.

### *Blood pressure*

A baseline blood pressure (BP) measurement is taken at this point, and measurements taken later in the pregnancy will be compared to this.

The average healthy BP range for a younger mother (35 or under) is 110/70–120/80. Blood pressure above 140/90 can indicate **pre-eclampsia** in a mother whose BP is usually within the average range.

**Key term**

**Caesarean section** An operation in which a surgeon delivers a child by cutting through the wall of the mother's abdomen.

**Figure 1.16** A baby's heartbeat will be monitored

**Key term**

**Pre-eclampsia** A condition causing high BP in pregnancy and after the labour. It must be monitored closely and can be serious if not treated.

## Blood tests

Blood tests are taken when booking the mother into the maternity system, to check for the following and to reveal possible problems:

- Anaemia – this condition can cause tiredness and listlessness, due to a lack of iron. Folic acid and iron tablets may be needed.
- High blood sugar – this will reveal if the mother has diabetes. It is possible for diabetes to develop during the pregnancy and pass away afterwards.
- Blood group – this information is required in case a blood transfusion is needed during pregnancy or birth.
- German measles (rubella) – this will reveal whether the woman is immune to German measles, a very dangerous disease for the developing unborn baby. It can cause brain damage, deafness and blindness in the baby.
- Hepatitis B and C – without treatment, these conditions can cause liver disease.
- HIV – this can be passed from mother to baby via the placenta in pregnancy or via breastfeeding after birth.

## Examination of the uterus

Examination of the uterus is routinely performed throughout a pregnancy, by both doctors and midwives. The doctor or midwife will place a gloved index and middle finger into the vagina up to the cervix. They will assess:

- how soft the cervix is
- whether there is any thinning (effacement) or opening (dilation) of the cervix
- the position of the cervix, whether posterior (facing the tailbone) or anterior (facing the front)
- how far into the pelvis the baby has descended
- which way the baby is facing (presentation).

## Urine test

A urine test can also reveal potential problems during pregnancy:

- Protein in the urine might mean that the mother has an infection. It can also indicate the beginning of a serious condition such as pre-eclampsia.
- Glucose (sugar) in the urine can indicate diabetes, which will need to be controlled by diet and sometimes also by taking insulin.
- Ketones might be present if a mother has been vomiting excessively (known as hyperemesis). In this case, hospitalisation is needed, and fluids and glucose might need to be replaced via a drip. Without treatment, a condition called ketosis can occur, which can lead to a coma and even death, so this test is very important.

- STIs, which can be harmful for an unborn baby. These infections can be caught before or during pregnancy. They can be more serious when caught during pregnancy, and even life-threatening for the mother/baby.

  Some STIs, including chlamydia and gonorrhoea, can be treated and cured with antibiotics. Some cannot be cured. These conditions may be treated to reduce the risk of them being passed to the baby.

### Weight check

Women are weighed when they are first booked in to record a baseline weight. The weight of the mother can then be tracked and monitored against this throughout the pregnancy.

- If a woman gains more weight than expected, it could be a sign of pre-eclampsia, and treatment will be necessary.
- Weight loss could indicate that the baby has stopped growing and can also be a sign of illness in the mother. Women are expected to gain 10–12.5 kg during a normal, healthy pregnancy.

## 2.2 Screening and diagnostic tests

**Screening tests** are offered to all pregnant mothers. They reveal whether a baby has a high chance of being born with certain conditions.

When a screening test reveals this, a **diagnostic test** will be offered to establish whether or not the baby has the condition.

Screening tests are carried out first, because diagnostic testing carries a risk of miscarriage, and screening tests are safe for the mother and baby.

### The reasons for screening tests and what conditions they can identify

#### Ultrasound scans

##### Dating scan

Around 8–14 weeks into pregnancy, an ultrasound dating scan is offered to the mother, with a professional called a sonographer. It is usually carried out in a hospital ultrasound department. This scan checks:

- how far along the pregnancy is, enabling the sonographer to work out the baby's due date
- the baby's development
- whether more than one baby is expected
- that the baby is growing in the right place.

**Test your knowledge**

1 List the six types of routine tests/checks carried out at antenatal clinics.
2 Write down the purpose for each type of test/check.

**Key terms**

**Screening test** Identifies whether an unborn baby is more or less likely to have certain conditions at birth.

**Diagnostic test** Used to diagnose certain medical conditions in an unborn baby.

**Activity**

With a partner, discuss the advantages of knowing a baby's due date for:

- the mother/parents
- the medical team caring for the mother and baby.

Some abnormalities may also be detected, such as neural tube defects (e.g. spina bifida).

During an ultrasound scan, the sonographer passes the ultrasound probe backwards and forwards over the skin to build up an image of the baby. Gel is applied to the abdomen (tummy) to form a bond between the probe and the skin for a better result.

### Anomaly scan

This is a more detailed scan, generally carried out between 18 and 21 weeks of pregnancy. It checks for major physical abnormalities in the baby but cannot find everything that might be wrong. The scan looks at the baby's:

- bones
- heart
- brain
- spinal cord
- face
- kidneys
- abdomen.

The sonographer will look for the following 11 conditions:

- anencephaly
- open spina bifida
- cleft lip
- diaphragmatic hernia
- gastroschisis
- exomphalos
- serious cardiac abnormalities
- bilateral renal agenesis
- lethal skeletal dysplasia
- Edwards' syndrome, or Trisomy 18 (t18)
- Patau's syndrome, or Trisomy 13 (t13).

Most babies will be developing normally, but serious problems are identified in a small number of cases.

Some of the problems identified may mean the baby will need treatment or surgery after birth. In rare cases, no treatment is possible, and the baby will die during pregnancy or soon after birth.

If a scan picks up a problem, further tests may be offered.

The NHS offers a two-dimensional black and white image, giving a side view of the baby, at the anomaly scan. This is treasured by many parents.

**Stretch activity**

Mothers can choose whether or not to have scans – not everyone wants to find out if their baby has a problem. If a mother decides against having a scan, her antenatal care will continue as normal in all other respects.

With a partner, discuss why some women might choose to have a scan and some might not.

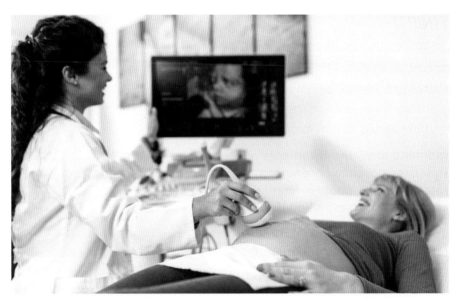

**Figure 1.17** Image of a baby given at the anomaly scan

## Nuchal fold translucency (NT) test

Nuchal translucency refers to a fluid under the skin at the back of the unborn baby's neck. The amount of fluid present can be measured using ultrasound; babies with Down's syndrome (Trisomy 21, t21) often have an increased amount of this fluid. All mothers are offered a test to look for this at around week 11–13 of pregnancy, to assess whether their baby is likely to have Down's syndrome.

Screening can only estimate the level of risk – it cannot determine whether or not the baby definitely has Down's syndrome. Other tests (see below) can accurately diagnose Down's syndrome, but as these carry a small risk of miscarriage, the obstetrician will carry out a screening test first to see whether a diagnostic test should be offered. A blood test may also be carried out alongside the NT test.

Not all mothers will choose to have the NT test, and not all mothers who are given a result with a high likelihood of Down's syndrome will go on to have a diagnostic test. This is the mother's decision.

## Triple test

The triple test is carried out between 10 and 14 weeks of pregnancy. It assesses the chance of having a baby with Down's syndrome, Edwards' syndrome and Patau's syndrome.

If a screening test shows a higher chance of having a baby with any of these syndromes, the mother will be offered further tests to find out if their baby has the condition.

### *Non-Invasive Prenatal Testing (NIPT)*

NIPT is a screening blood test that assesses the likelihood of having a baby with Down's syndrome, Edwards' syndrome or Patau's syndrome.

- It can be carried out from week 10 of pregnancy, which is earlier than alternative tests.
- It is also more accurate and does not carry a risk of miscarriage.

A blood sample is taken from the mother's arm, and fragments of the baby's DNA within this are analysed for possible chromosomal abnormalities. If the risk of chromosomal abnormality is found to be high, a diagnostic test such as chorionic villus sampling (CVS) or amniocentesis will be offered.

NHS hospitals do not generally offer NIPT, therefore most parents wanting the test will need to pay to have it done privately.

Some parents choose to have NIPT before deciding to have a diagnostic test that carries a risk of miscarriage, because when a high-risk NIPT result is given, it is likely that the diagnostic test will also be positive. If the NIPT is negative, the parents may decide against a diagnostic test.

## The reasons for diagnostic tests and what conditions they can identify

If a screening test reveals that there may be an issue, one of the following diagnostic tests will be offered.

### *Chorionic villus sampling*

This test checks if a baby has a genetic disorder, such as Down's syndrome, through the removal and testing of a small sample of cells from the placenta. The test is only offered if there is a high risk of a baby having a genetic condition, for example, if:

- an earlier antenatal screening test has indicated a problem
- the mother has had a previous pregnancy with these problems
- there is family history of a genetic condition.

CVS is usually carried out between weeks 11 and 14 of pregnancy.

### *Risks of CVS*

The test carries a risk of miscarriage, which occurs in between one and two per cent of women who have CVS. There is also a risk of infection, and for these reasons, not all mothers offered the test will decide to go ahead.

There is no cure for the majority of conditions detected via CVS. If a serious disorder is detected, the implications will be fully discussed. The mother may choose to continue with the pregnancy, while gathering information about the condition so she is fully prepared, or she may consider a termination.

## Amniocentesis

This procedure also tests for genetic disorders (Down's syndrome, Edwards' syndrome and Patau's syndrome, cystic fibrosis, muscular dystrophy, sickle cell disease and thalassaemia) and may be offered as an alternative to the CVS test (and in the same circumstances as the CVS test).

It is generally carried out between weeks 15 and 18 of pregnancy, when a small sample of amniotic fluid (the fluid that surrounds the baby in the womb) is removed for testing.

## Risks of amniocentesis

The risk of causing miscarriage is slightly reduced with amniocentesis when compared with CVS, but results cannot be given until a later stage of pregnancy. This creates more difficulties for the possibility of terminating the pregnancy if a problem is found.

## 2.3 The purpose and importance of antenatal (parenting) classes

Most mothers will start attending antenatal classes once a week, in the daytime or the evening, around weeks 30–32 of pregnancy. Those who are expecting twins will generally begin in week 24 of pregnancy, as the babies are more likely to be born early.

Classes are generally informal and fun, but there are local differences in provision. For example:

- Mothers might be offered two separate classes – one focusing on pregnancy, labour and birth, and another focusing on parenthood and baby care.
- Parents might only be offered antenatal classes on the NHS, but might choose to also attend a private parenting class.

Classes are generally run by a midwife.

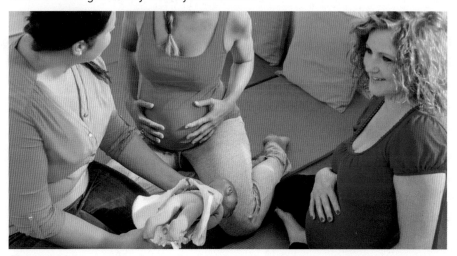

**Figure 1.18** Antenatal and parenting classes help mothers to prepare for the birth

## Prepares both parents for labour and parenthood

Antenatal and parenting classes usually help to prepare both parents for labour and parenthood by covering:

- what happens during labour and birth, so parents know what to expect
- how to cope with labour, including information about different types of pain relief and relaxation methods, such as breathing techniques
- information on different types of labour and birth (e.g. home birth, hospital birth), which helps a mother to create a personal birth plan and to discuss this with professionals
- information on different types of birth interventions, such as ventouse or forceps delivery (see section 2.9)
- caring for a baby (e.g. feeding, sleeping and bathing)
- the mother's health after the birth
- giving parents the chance to talk over any concerns, and perhaps meet key professionals who will care for the mother and baby during labour
- discussions of emotions and feelings during pregnancy, birth and after the birth, so that parents have realistic expectations
- how the father/partner can plan their participation in the birth and how to support the mother
- refresher classes for those who have already had a baby
- information about other sources of support.

**Figure 1.19** Classes are a chance for parents to discuss feelings and concerns

## Promotes healthy lifestyle and diet

Antenatal classes also provide advice on staying fit and healthy during pregnancy through:

- safe exercise – the NHS has this advice for pregnant woman:

    *The more active and fit you stay during pregnancy, the easier it will be for you to adapt to your changing shape and weight gain. It will also help you to cope with labour and get back into shape after the birth.*

(www.nhs.uk/pregnancy/keeping-well/exercise/)

- a healthy diet: pregnant women are advised to follow the Eatwell Guide (see Unit R059, section 3.1) to ensure they eat a balanced diet
- learning about the negative impact of smoking, alcohol and recreational drugs during pregnancy and after the birth
- learning about the benefits of breastfeeding.

### Foods to avoid during pregnancy

Most food and drink are safe for women during pregnancy, but information will be given on foods to avoid, such as:

- unpasteurised milk, or foods made from it (e.g. soft goats' cheese)
- mould-ripened soft cheese with a white coating on the outside (e.g. brie)

**Figure 1.20** Some soft cheeses should be avoided during pregnancy

- soft blue cheeses (e.g. gorgonzola)
- raw or undercooked meat
- liver and liver products
- pâté
- game meats
- raw or partially cooked eggs that are not stamped British Lion
- duck, goose or quail eggs unless cooked through until the whites and yolks are solid
- swordfish, marlin, shark, raw shellfish
- alcohol
- liquorice root.

There are other foods and drinks that should be limited in pregnancy:

- oily fish should be limited to two portions per week
- no more than two tuna steaks or four medium-sized cans of tuna per week
- caffeine should be limited to 200 mg per day
- no more than four cups of herbal tea per day
- high-dose multivitamin supplements and any supplements with vitamin A in them must be avoided.

Women are advised to be careful to ensure that fruit, vegetables and salad do not have soil on them, which could cause illness.

## Provides advice on feeding and caring for the baby

A very important part of antenatal classes is learning to care for a baby. This will include:

- feeding
- sleeping
- bathing.

### Why breast feeding is encouraged for at least the first two weeks

In the first few days after birth, mothers produce a concentrated form of milk called colostrum. The colostrum:

- is high in protein
- contains high levels of antibodies and immunoglobulins, two immune factors that protect newborns from viruses and bacteria
- is thick and usually a golden yellow colour.

No other milk has such concentrated immune boosters, so mothers are encouraged to provide this powerful first food.

**Research**

You may use the internet or textbooks to research these points:

1 Choose three foods to be avoided during pregnancy and find out the reason for this.
2 Choose three foods or drinks to be limited during pregnancy and find out the reason for this.

**Activity**

Find out more about private parenting classes by visiting this link:

**www.theparentandbaby coach.com**

- Scroll down and read the information.
- Click the link to explore online parenting courses.
- Now use a search engine to research the antenatal and parenting classes available in your local area.

A few days after birth, a mother will produce actual milk. This contains the exact quantities of fat, protein, carbohydrates and nutrients needed by the baby. This 'mature milk' also contains the immune factors, just at lower concentrations. So every day a baby is breastfed, it receives an additional immune boost.

Breastfeeding also helps mothers and babies to bond. Some mothers may continue breastfeeding after two weeks, and some may switch to formula feeds (see page 112).

**Stretch activity**

1 Imagine that a pregnant mother has told you that she isn't planning to attend antenatal classes because she's already read books on birth and parenting. Make a list of all the benefits of attending antenatal classes.
2 In a role play with a partner, explain and discuss what you would say to the mother to encourage her to attend.

## 2.4 The choices available for delivery

There are choices available when it comes to the delivery and birth, and there are advantages and disadvantages to each. To make the right choice, a mother needs the right information.

- The GP will normally be the first to provide information explaining the options.
- The mother can also talk the options over with her midwife at an early appointment, and with the leader of antenatal and parenting classes.

The following pages describe the choices available. Often, not all of the provision will be available within one local area. For example, some mothers may have a consultant-led unit nearby, while others may have a midwife or GP-led unit.

### Hospital birth

Types of hospital provision vary locally and can include:

- consultant-led units
- midwife- or GP-led units
- birthing centres (this environment is generally the most similar to home).

Delivery rooms in hospitals are becoming increasingly home-like and comfortable, with furniture such as soft chairs and beanbags. These enable mothers to change position, which can help with pain management. Warm baths and showers may also be available (most commonly in birthing centres), and these can also soothe and ease pain during early labour.

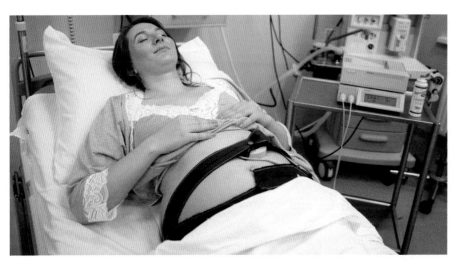

**Figure 1.21** Hospital delivery room

Maternity units increasingly offer birthing pools, which offer comfort and pain relief, and also enable a water birth if labour progresses normally. A water birth will need to be arranged ahead of time as part of the birthing plan, because of the limited number of pools available.

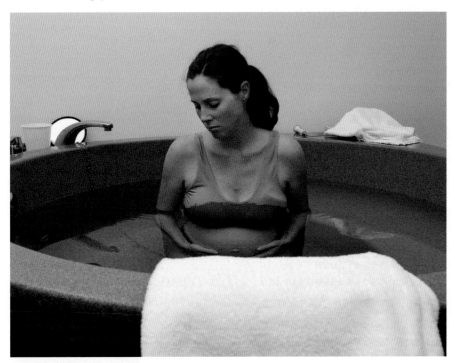

**Figure 1.22** Birthing pools are increasingly available

Advantages of a hospital birth include the following:

- Highly trained staff and equipment are available should an emergency arise – this could save a baby's life and is reassuring for parents.
- Some types of pain relief can only be given in hospital.
- Forceps, ventouse and Caesarean section deliveries can only be carried out in hospital (see below).

- Midwives are on hand after the birth to help with concerns and issues.
- The demands of the mother's home life are left behind.

Other considerations/disadvantages with a hospital birth:

- Interventions such as forceps or ventouse are more likely in hospital.
- Older siblings will not be part of the birthing experience.
- A mother is less likely to be looked after by a midwife she knows.
- A mother may feel more relaxed at home.

## Home birth

Home birth is an option when the pregnancy is normal, and mother and baby are both well. Support is given by a midwife, who attends during labour. If the labour does not progress normally or the mother needs help, the midwife's role is then to arrange a transfer to hospital.

Advantages of a home birth include the following:

- The mother is in familiar, relaxing surroundings.
- Labour is not interrupted by travelling to hospital.
- If the new baby has older siblings, they will not need to be separated from the mother as she gives birth, and they can be involved in the labour/birth.
- The mother is more likely to be looked after by a midwife she has seen throughout the pregnancy.
- An intervention such as forceps or ventouse is less likely than when giving birth in hospital.

Other considerations/disadvantages with a home birth:

- A transfer to a hospital may be needed if there are complications.
- The NHS report that for women having their second or subsequent baby, a planned home birth is as safe as having a baby in hospital or a midwife-led unit. However, for women having their first baby, home birth slightly increases the risk of a poor outcome for the baby (from 5 in 1000 for a hospital birth to 9 in 1000 – almost one per cent – for a home birth). Poor outcomes include death of the baby and problems that might affect the baby's quality of life.
- Epidurals (for pain relief) are not given at home.
- A midwife or doctor might advise that a hospital birth is safer for a mother and baby in some circumstances.

### Domino scheme

The Domino scheme is operated by some hospitals. It involves community midwives providing antenatal care and then meeting the mother at the hospital for the delivery. In many cases, the midwife is able to assess the mother closely during labour, so the move to hospital will not be made until close to the delivery. If all is well, the mother and baby will be able to leave hospital after six hours. This means that the hospital stay can be shortened.

**Research**

Find out more about the choices available for delivery by visiting this NHS website:

**www.nhs.uk/conditions/ pregnancy-and-baby/ pages/where-can-i-give-birth.aspx**

- Read the information and watch the video clip.
- Now follow this NHS link, reading the advice and watching the video clips about home birth:

**www.nhs.uk/video/Pages/ Givingbirthathome.aspx**

## Private care

Some parents pay for a private hospital or independent midwife, rather than accessing free NHS provision. This decision might be made by some parents who can afford it because they feel that the standard of the provision is higher than that of the NHS.

A private hospital is also a popular choice for families who are in the public eye. As these hospitals are not public buildings, it is easier for their privacy to be protected.

## Independent midwives

You were introduced to independent midwives in section 2.1. An independent midwife might not undertake all of the responsibilities of NHS midwives, so mothers may in fact use both services. For example, an independent midwife may have fulfilled their role after giving support following the birth. If advice on feeding is needed after a few weeks, the mother might then contact an NHS midwife for advice.

## 2.5 The role of the birth partner in supporting the mother through pregnancy and birth

A **birth partner** is someone who will support the mother throughout pregnancy and the birth. This includes attending antenatal classes. A mother's birth partner may be the baby's father, her partner, a family member or a friend.

### The benefits of having a birth partner

Pregnancy and birth are significant events in a woman's life and a time of many changes. Women's bodies are changing, and women are likely to experience tiredness, morning sickness and may feel emotional.

It is normal to feel apprehensive about the birth and caring for a newborn, so it's very important for a mother to have support from someone they can rely on. During antenatal (and parenting) classes, a birthing partner will learn how to offer both physical and emotional support.

### Physical support

The birth partner can:

- help the mother during pregnancy by providing practical support with tasks if the mother is feeling tired, such as helping with grocery shopping
- help the mother during labour and birth – by massaging the back, shoulders or legs, supporting the mother's body, timing the contractions, offering drinks, snacks or ice cubes, sponging the mother down and helping the mother to find a comfortable position

> **Key term**
>
> **Birth partner** Someone who will attend antenatal classes and support the mother throughout pregnancy and the birth.

- learning relaxation and breathing techniques alongside the mother – they can then encourage the mother to use the techniques by participating alongside her during labour and birth.

## Emotional support

The birth partner can:

- be emotionally supportive if the mother is anxious about coping with birth
- help the mother during labour and birth – by giving encouragement, talking or finding ways to pass the time and making sure health professionals are aware of the birthing plan
- helping with arrangements at home – for instance, by arranging childcare for older siblings when a mother goes into labour.

## 2.6 Methods of pain relief when in labour

It is natural for mothers to be concerned about handling the pain of childbirth, so it is important that they consider the options for pain relief when they make their birth plan. Each option has its own advantages and disadvantages.

Breathing and relaxation techniques learnt in antenatal classes are used alongside the following pain relief options.

### Epidural anaesthetic

This is a local anaesthetic that numbs the nerves that carry the pain impulses from the birth canal to the brain. It can provide total pain relief, but it is not always 100 per cent effective. It is often used when a mother is experiencing a very long or painful labour, or when a mother becomes distressed.

An epidural can only be given by an anaesthetist in hospital:

- The mother lies on her side or sits curled up.
- Local anaesthetic is used to numb the back, then a needle is inserted.
- A tube passes through the needle into the back, near the nerves that carry pain impulses from the uterus.
- Drugs, usually a mixture of local anaesthetic and opioid, are administered through this tube.
- It takes about 10 minutes to administer an epidural, and up to another 15 minutes for it to work. It can then be topped up if necessary.

An epidural does not usually cause sickness or drowsiness, but the mother's contractions and the baby's heart rate will need to be continuously monitored. Possible side effects include:

- legs feeling heavy
- BP dropping (this is rare)

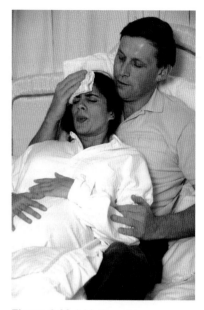

**Figure 1.23** A birth partner supports the mother during labour

- prolonged second stage of labour as contractions may not be felt, leading to increased likelihood of assisted delivery
- difficulty passing urine
- a headache (this can be treated)
- a sore back for a day or two afterwards.

## Gas and air (Entonox)

This mixture of oxygen and nitrous oxide gas does not remove all the pain, but it can help to reduce it.

- Mothers breathe in the gas and air through a mask or mouthpiece which they hold themselves – this gives them a sense of control.
- It works within about 20 seconds, so a deep slow breath will be taken as a contraction begins.
- There may be a light-headed sensation, and some mothers decide to stop using it as they may feel sick, sleepy or unable to concentrate.
- A painkilling injection can be given alongside if this pain relief is not sufficient.

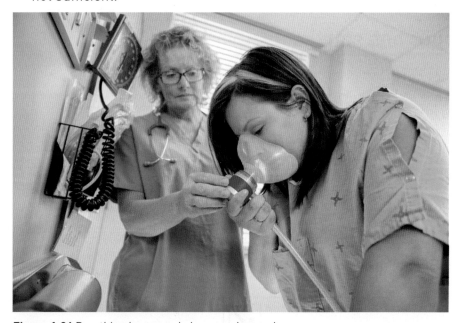

**Figure 1.24** Breathing in gas and air can reduce pain

## Pethidine

This opiate-based drug is given by injection. It quickly makes the mother feel relaxed because it causes the muscles to relax. This makes pain more tolerable, but it does not take it away altogether. Used in early labour, it can help the mother to settle and rest.

It cannot be used too close to birth because the mother might not be alert enough, and it could also cause the baby to become sleepy. This could negatively affect feeding and even breathing.

Pethidine can cause some mothers to feel sick or disorientated.

## TENS

TENS stands for 'transcutaneous electrical nerve stimulation'. A TENS machine is a small device that has leads connected to sticky pads called electrodes.

- The electrodes are attached to the mother's skin. Small electrical impulses are delivered – these give a tingling sensation.
- The impulses reduce the pain signals going to the spinal cord and brain, relieving pain and relaxing muscles.
- It is possible that the electrical impulses also stimulate the production of endorphins – the body's 'natural painkillers'.

For most people, TENS carries no side effects (there are special pads for people with allergies), but it should not be used:

- if the mother has a pacemaker or another type of electrical or metal implant
- if the mother has epilepsy or a heart problem
- in some cases early in pregnancy.

## 2.7 The signs that labour has started

Signs that labour has started include the following:

- A show – not all women experience a show, but it can occur when a plug of mucus that has sealed off the uterus during pregnancy comes away from the cervix as it dilates (gets wider). This will be stained with blood, but no blood should be lost.
- The waters break – the bag of amniotic fluid around the baby bursts, causing anything from a trickle to a gush of liquid from the vagina. It is now time to go to hospital (or chosen birth option) because there is a risk of infection for the baby.
- Contractions – the uterus muscles start to contract and release. Contractions gradually become stronger and occur increasingly closer together.

### Test your knowledge

1 What is the name for when a plug of mucus that has sealed off the uterus during pregnancy comes away from the cervix as it dilates, providing a sign that labour has started?
2 When a woman's waters break, what is the name of the fluid that escapes from the vagina?
3 When contractions start, which muscles contract and release?

### Activity

With a partner, go online and search for three different TENS machines for sale.

- Read and compare the information about each machine. Are all the advantages and disadvantages explained?
- Discuss with your partner.

### Research

Visit this NHS webpage:

www.nhs.uk/pregnancy/labour-and-birth/signs-of-labour/signs-that-labour-has-begun/

- Read the information 'What contractions feel like'.
- You will also learn about Braxton Hicks contractions, which women may experience towards the end of the pregnancy.

## 2.8 The three stages of labour and their physiological changes

Every labour is different, but all pass through three common stages. These are divided into:

- Stage 1 – labour
- Stage 2 – birth
- Stage 3 – delivery of placenta and membranes.

### Stage 1 – Neck of the uterus opens

You learnt about the signs that labour has started in section 2.7. As the neck of the uterus continues to open:

- More pain relief is required as the contractions become stronger, more regular and longer-lasting. A warm bath can help.
- Mothers are encouraged to actively move around in an upright position.
- The cervix gradually dilates to 8–10 cm wide.
- If the head of the baby is not already engaged in the mother's pelvis, it will move into position.
- As the end of this stage approaches, intense contractions can cause the mother to feel agitated, and to vomit, sweat or shiver. Due to pressure from the baby's head, she may lose bladder and/or bowel control.
- When contractions get even closer together, stronger and more intense, the mother enters the **transition stage** that leads into the second stage of labour.

### Stage 2 – Birth of the baby

This stage starts when the cervix becomes fully dilated at 10 cm and ends when the baby has been born.

- The vagina and the open cervix now form a single passage known as the birth canal. The head of the baby moves into the birth canal.
- The mother begins to push with each contraction, to help move the baby down the birth canal. This can be exhausting, and she will need to rest between contractions.
- When the baby's head can be seen (crowning), it is time to stop pushing so that the head is born gradually and safely. Instead, the mother will pant or blow out, to control her breathing. The head must be born slowly to avoid the mother's skin tearing between the vagina and rectum (the perineum). A cut (an episiotomy) may need to be made if the perineum does not stretch enough.

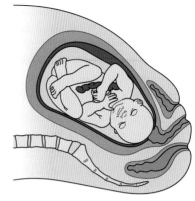

**Figure 1.25** The first stage of labour

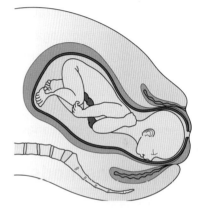

**Figure 1.26** Diagram of a baby with the head engaged

### Key term

**Transition stage** This links the end of the first stage of labour and the beginning of the second stage of labour.

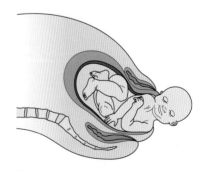

**Figure 1.27** The second stage of labour

- The hard work of labour is over once the head has been born, as the body can be turned so that the shoulders are delivered one at a time. This will be followed by the rest of the baby's body, which slides out easily. If the baby needs to have mucus removed from its airways or to be given oxygen, this can be done as soon as the head is born, before the rest of the body is delivered.

- Finally, the umbilical cord will be clamped and cut. The father/ partner might cut the cord themselves. The baby is likely to be placed on the mother for skin-to-skin contact. Some blood from the birth and a protective layer of oily vernix (see section 3.1.1) are likely to be present on the baby's skin.

### Stage 3 – Delivery of placenta

In the shortest stage of labour which follows the birth:

- Contractions begin again, and these push the placenta out.

- An injection of syntocinon may be given to stimulate contractions and speed up the process. This helps to prevent the loss of blood and is helpful if the mother is exhausted.

- If a tear occurred in the perineum or a cut was made, it will be sewn up under local anaesthetic.

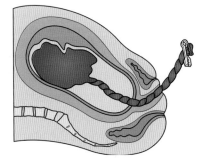

**Figure 1.28** The third stage of labour

## 2.9 The methods of assisted birth

There are various methods of delivery. Some will be planned in advance, while others become necessary if help is needed during labour.

The NHS reports that about one in eight women has an assisted birth in which forceps or a ventouse suction cup are used to help deliver the baby's head. This can be because:

- there are concerns about the baby's heart rate
- the baby is in an awkward position
- the mother is too exhausted.

The procedures are safe but are only used when necessary.

### Forceps

Forceps looks similar to tongs – a curved metal instrument that fits around a baby's head. They are carefully positioned, then joined together at the handles.

- As the mother pushes with a contraction, an obstetrician gently pulls to help deliver the baby.

- Some forceps are designed to turn the baby to the right position to be born, if this is necessary.

- Forceps are usually more successful than ventouse (see below), but are more likely to result in vaginal tearing.

## Ventouse

A ventouse (vacuum extractor) is a plastic or metal cup that fits firmly on the baby's head and is attached by suction.

- As the mother pushes with a contraction, an obstetrician gently pulls to help deliver the baby.
- The process leaves a small swelling on the baby's head, which will disappear quickly. The cup may also leave a temporary bruise.
- A ventouse is not used with babies born before week 34 of pregnancy because the head is too soft.

## Episiotomy

An episiotomy is an incision made in the perineum (the tissue between the vaginal opening and the anus). It is usually performed during second stage of labour if it is necessary to quickly enlarge the opening for the baby to pass through.

## Risks of assisted birth

These include:

- vaginal tearing or episiotomy
- a higher chance of having a vaginal tear that involves the muscle or wall of the anus or rectum
- higher risk of blood clots, leaking urine and anal incontinence.

A catheter is sometimes needed for a short period. This is a small hollow tube that is inserted through the urethra into the bladder to remove urine. It is used to empty the bladder so that a doctor can examine the mother to confirm that an assisted birth is necessary. A catheter is also used during an epidural when a mother might be numb to the sensation that her bladder is full, and when she has to stay in bed so cannot get up to urinate. A catheter is uncomfortable when it is inserted, and some women find it difficult to urinate once it is removed.

## Elective/emergency Caesarean section

A Caesarean section is an operation to deliver a baby through a cut made in the abdomen and womb.

This may be recommended as an elective (planned) procedure, or done in an emergency if a vaginal birth becomes unsafe. Reasons for a Caesarean include:

- the baby being in the breech position (feet first)
- a low-lying placenta (placenta praevia)
- pre-eclampsia
- infections such as STIs and untreated HIV
- the baby not getting enough oxygen and nutrients so needs to be delivered immediately
- labour not progressing
- excessive vaginal bleeding.

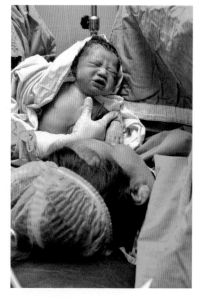

**Figure 1.29** A Caesarean may be recommended as an elective procedure

### Practice question

Couple Daniel and Melanie are expecting their first baby. The pregnancy is considered to be low risk. A midwife will look after Melanie and her baby throughout the phase of antenatal care, during labour and during the birth.

When else will the midwife look after Melanie and the baby, and for how long?     [2 marks]

Caesareans are a major operation and there are risks, so they are not suitable for every mother. Around one in every four to five pregnant women in the UK has a Caesarean.

## Topic area 3 Postnatal checks, postnatal care and the conditions for development

It is extremely helpful for you to be familiar with the **postnatal** checks, postnatal care and conditions for development. This will enable you to offer understanding and support to both parents and baby in the early days and weeks after the birth.

**Key term**
**Postnatal** After birth.

### Getting started

Write a list of all of the ideal conditions you think babies need to thrive and develop well, for example, warmth.

## 3.1 Postnatal checks

### The postnatal checks that are carried out on the baby immediately after birth and the reasons why

Straight after the birth, the doctor and/or midwife will carry out some routine checks to find out if the baby has any obvious physical problems.

#### Apgar score

The Apgar score is used to evaluate the physical condition of a newborn, by assessing five vital signs: heartbeat, breathing, muscle tone, reflex response (when the foot or nostril is stimulated) and colour.

The score is used to assess how well the baby is doing outside the mother's womb, and whether it needs medical assistance. This quick assessment is carried out one minute after birth, and again at five minutes after birth. If a problem is identified, reassessment may continue every five minutes.

**Table 1.1** An example of the Apgar Table

| Indicator | 0 points | 1 point | 2 points | 1 min | 5 mins | 10 mins |
|---|---|---|---|---|---|---|
| Heart rate (bpm) | absent | < 100 | > 100 | | | |
| Respiratory effort | absent | weak cry | strong good cry | | | |
| Muscle tone | limp | some flexion | well flexed | | | |
| Reflex response | no response | some motion | cry | | | |
| Colour | blue/pale | body pink, limbs blue | pink | | | |
| | | | Total | | | |

Scores are given out of 10 (each sign can score between zero and two):

- The majority of healthy babies score nine – many of them lose a point because they have blue extremities, and this is a condition that can last several hours after birth.
- In hospital, a paediatrician will be informed if there is a score of six or under after five minutes. (Low scores at one minute are not so concerning, as many babies will score higher by five minutes.)
- Babies who score between five and seven will be showing signs of mild asphyxia (lack of oxygen in the blood) and may need treatment.
- A score of between three and four indicates moderate asphyxia that will certainly need treatment.
- A baby scoring between zero and two has severe asphyxia and will need emergency resuscitation.

## Skin

A newborn baby's skin can be damaged easily because it is very thin. It will take a month or so for it to develop and mature into a protective barrier – longer if a baby is premature. A baby's skin will be checked for birthmarks.

### Salmon patches (stork marks)

These are flat red or pink patches that appear on the eyelids, neck or forehead at birth. They can be more noticeable when a baby cries because they fill with blood and become darker, and most fade completely in a few months.

On the forehead or the back of the neck, they can remain for four years or longer.

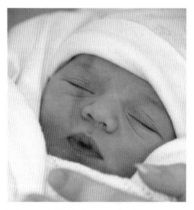

**Figure 1.30** Salmon patches may appear on the baby's skin at birth

### Blue-grey spots

These are bluish patches of darker pigment, appearing most commonly over the bottom and on black skin. They can be mistaken for bruises but are completely harmless. They usually disappear by the age of four.

### Infantile haemangiomas (strawberry marks)

These are raised marks on the skin that are usually red and can appear anywhere on the body. They grow in the first six months but then shrink and disappear, usually by seven years of age.

### Vernix

This is the white, waxy substance that covers a baby's skin while it is in the womb. Newborns will have this on their skin at birth. It is a natural moisturiser and provides a protective layer that helps to prevent infection, so it should be left to absorb naturally into the skin.

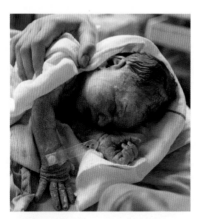

**Figure 1.31** Newborns will have vernix on their skin at birth

If a baby is overdue, the vernix may have been absorbed while in the womb, leading to dry and cracked skin.

- Avoid creams or lotions, as these can irritate the baby's skin.
- The top layer of skin will peel off on its own over a few days, revealing perfectly healthy skin underneath.

### Lanugo

During pregnancy, at around 22 weeks, a baby begins to become covered in lanugo – soft, fine hair that is usually unpigmented (it does not have colour). It is thought that this downy hair helps to keep the baby's body at the right temperature.

Lanugo is generally shed during months 7–8 of pregnancy, but it is sometimes present in premature babies and full-term newborns. This is no cause for concern though, and the lanugo disappears within a few days or weeks.

After new parents have had time to cuddle their baby and have skin-to-skin contact, which is important for bonding, some more physical checks will be done, and these are outlined below.

Within 72 hours of a baby being born, all parents in the UK are also offered a thorough physical examination of their baby, and after that there will continue to be regular checks to monitor a baby's growth and development. This is extremely important, as it enables any problems to be identified and treated as early as possible.

### Weight

The baby's weight will be recorded in a Personal Child Health Record (the 'red book'), which is given to all parents. A digital app version is also available.

A full-term baby usually weighs 2.7–4.1 kg (6–9 lb). The weight is tracked on centile charts which show the expected pattern of growth of a healthy baby, so that comparisons can be made over the coming weeks and months.

Steady weight gain is an important sign that a baby is healthy and feeding well. It is normal for babies to lose some of their birth weight within the first few days, but this should soon be regained – usually within two weeks. Support will be given by a health professional if this does not happen.

Boys and girls have different centile charts because their growth pattern is slightly different. Baby boys are often heavier and longer than baby girls.

**Figure 1.32** Recording a baby's weight

## Length

As with weight, length is also recorded on centile charts, which allows health professionals to see how the baby is growing. The length of a full-term newborn is usually 50–53 cm.

## Head circumference

The shape of the baby's head is assessed, and the circumference measured. These measurements will also be used to track the baby's development over the coming weeks and months.

A squashed appearance is common, as a result of the baby being squeezed through the birth canal. This usually resolves itself within two days.

# The checks that are carried out on the baby within one to five days of birth and the reasons why

## Physical examination

All parents are offered a thorough physical examination for their baby within five days of giving birth. The examination includes screening tests to find out if the baby has any problems with their eyes, heart, hips and, in boys, testicles.

The aim is to spot any problems early so treatment can be started as soon as possible. Usually, nothing of concern is found.

If possible problems are found, babies may be referred for more tests. Some parts of the examination might be a little uncomfortable for babies, but do not cause pain.

## Feet

The toes will be counted and checked for webbing.

The natural resting position of the baby's feet and ankles will be observed to check for talipes (clubfoot) – a condition in which the front half of the foot turns in and down. Talipes may already have been identified in an ultrasound scan.

## Fingers

Fingers will be counted and checked for webbing.

The baby's palms will be checked to see if two creases (palmar creases) run across them. A single palmar crease is sometimes associated with Down's syndrome.

## Hips

A health professional will check the baby for 'developmental dysplasia of the hip' – this is a condition in which the hip joints have not formed properly. This can result in joint problems or a limp if it is not identified and treated. Around 1 or 2 in 1000 babies are born with the condition.

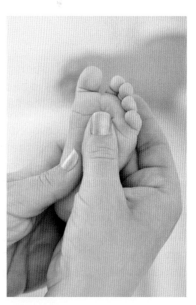

**Figure 1.33** Examining feet for webbing and clubfoot

## Eyes

Eye tests do not reveal how well a baby can actually see – they allow health professionals to check for cataracts and other conditions, by assessing the appearance and movement of the eyes.

This involves shining a light into the eyes to check a reflex. If a baby has cataracts, there will be a clouding of the transparent lens inside the eye.

The NHS reports that around 2 or 3 in every 10,000 babies are born with problems with their eyes that require treatment.

## Heart

The health professional will observe the baby, feeling the baby's pulses, and listen to their heart with a stethoscope.

Sometimes heart murmurs are picked up. A heart murmur is where the heartbeat has an extra or unusual sound caused by a disturbed blood flow through the heart. Heart murmurs are common in babies.

The heart is normal in almost all cases where a murmur is heard. But according to the NHS, about 8 in 1000 babies have congenital heart disease that needs treatment.

## Testicles in boys

Baby boys are checked to make sure their testicles are in the right place. During pregnancy, the testicles form inside the baby's body. They may not drop down into the scrotum until a few months after birth.

The NHS reports that around 2 to 6 in 100 baby boys have testicles that descend partially or not at all. This needs to be treated to prevent possible problems later in life, such as reduced fertility.

## Fontanelle

A baby's head has soft spots, called the fontanelles, between the bones in the skull. This is because the skull bones have not yet fused (joined) together when the baby is born.

These soft spots are covered by a tough protective membrane, and there is one on the top of the head near the front, and a smaller one towards the back. They will be checked, but it will be a year or more before the bones join together.

## Heel prick test (blood spot test)

The heel prick test is a screening test that helps to identify several rare but serious diseases with a small blood sample. This includes cystic fibrosis (CF) and sickle cell disease.

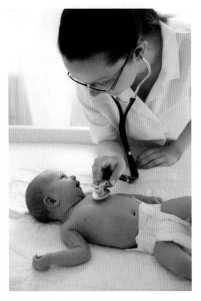

**Figure 1.34** A health professional checks the baby's heart

## Test your knowledge

1 What does the Apgar score evaluate?
2 What is vernix?
3 What is lanugo?
4 What does a centile chart track?

## 3.2 Postnatal care of the mother and baby

As you have learnt, having a baby is a very significant life event. A new arrival brings lots of enjoyment, but parents will also be making lots of adjustments to their usual lifestyle, and there will also be an impact on other close family members, such as siblings. The support needed depends on the individual baby and family, but postnatal provision is very important for everyone's well-being.

### The role of the health visitor in supporting the new family

A health visitor is a qualified nurse or midwife who has had extra training. Their job is to give all families support, from pregnancy up until children are aged five.

The Government's Healthy Child Programme offers every family regular contact with a health professional to make sure that their child is healthy and developing normally, and to support both parents to care well for their child. In 2021, the blog of Public Health England stated that:

> There is national commitment to modernise the programme over the next few years.

(www.gov.uk)

### *Information, advice and support the health visitor will provide*

Generally, a mother and baby will be cared for by local midwives until around 10 days after the baby is born. At this point, a health visitor will visit them at home for the first time. Health visitors often:

- advise on all aspects of baby care and childcare, including feeding, sleeping (including safe sleeping – see below – and sleep routines) and development
- run clinics (sometimes with GPs) offering important baby health and development reviews and vaccinations
- give advice and suggest where to find help if a family member is struggling with mental health
- put parents in touch with groups where they can meet other parents
- are available for parents to talk to about any issues to do with their child, but if the child is ill and likely to need treatment, they should see their GP.

**Research**

Visit this NHS webpage and watch the video for new parents called 'What healthcare will we get from the NHS after birth?':

**www.nhs.uk/conditions/baby/support-and-services/your-6-week-postnatal-check/**

**Activity**

With a partner, discuss how you think parents may feel about the first home visit by the health visitor.

## Safe sleeping – SIDS and how to reduce the risk

There has been much research into how sleeping position and bedding (including mattresses) may be a factor in cases of Sudden Infant Death Syndrome (SIDS).

SIDS occurs when a seemingly healthy baby or toddler dies unexpectedly in their sleep, with no medical explanation. This affects around 300 babies in the UK each year. The NHS advises that to prevent SIDS, babies should sleep on a mattress that is:

- firm
- flat
- waterproof
- in good condition.

Table 1.2 provides the complete list of advice given to parents for the prevention of SIDS.

**Table 1.2** Advice given to parents for the prevention of SIDS

| Do | Do not |
|---|---|
| • Always place your baby on their back to sleep. <br> • Place your baby in the 'feet to foot' position (with their feet touching the end of the cot, Moses basket, or pram). <br> • Keep your baby's head uncovered. Their blanket should be tucked in no higher than their shoulders. <br> • Let your baby sleep in a cot or Moses basket in the same room as you for the first six months. <br> • Use a mattress that is firm, flat, waterproof and in good condition. <br> • Breastfeed your baby (if you can). | • Smoke during pregnancy or let anyone smoke in the same room as your baby (both before and after birth). <br> • Sleep on a bed, sofa or armchair with your baby. This is even more dangerous if you or your partner smoke or take drugs, or if you have been drinking alcohol. <br> • Let your baby get too hot or too cold. A room temperature of 16–20 °C, with light bedding or a lightweight baby sleeping bag, will provide a comfortable sleeping environment for your baby. |

You'll learn more about sleep in section 3.3.

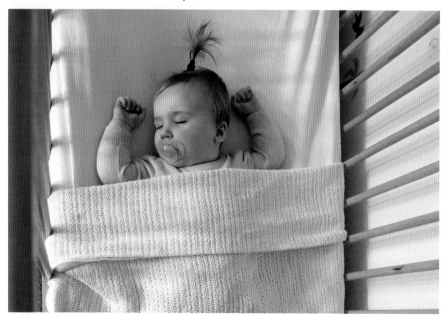

**Figure 1.35** Babies should sleep on their backs in the 'feet to foot' position, with their head uncovered

**Research**

Visit the website of the Lullaby Trust which provides safe sleep advice:

**www.lullabytrust.org.uk/ safer-sleep-advice/what-is-sids/**

1 Read the information on the homepage.
2 At the bottom of the page in the Downloads section, choose one of the three guides to read.

## How partner, family and friends can provide physical and emotional support

### Support from partner

The partner of the mother has a very significant role, and it is important that they have time to bond with the new baby alongside the mother.

They may also be the person closest to the mother and best placed to support her through the early days and weeks of motherhood, which can be difficult. It can take a great deal of time and energy to take care of a new baby. But the mother needs to take care of herself too, in order to stay fit and healthy, and in some cases to recover from the birth. The father/partner should ensure that the mother has the help and support she needs to achieve this.

The responsibility and tiredness that come with looking after a new baby can also put a strain on the relationship between the mother and their partner. Family and friends can help to relieve this.

### Support from family and friends

Support from other family and friends can be a huge help to new parents, especially if their own relationship comes under pressure as they adjust to their new responsibilities. Practical help and advice are both valuable, from helping with the shopping to sharing childcare tips.

Some new parents need a lot of support from family and friends who have more experience in the care of babies and children.

## The purpose of the mother's '6 week postnatal check' with the GP

Mothers are offered a postnatal check with a GP six to eight weeks after giving birth to make sure they are feeling well and are recovering properly. The following usually happens:

- Mothers are asked how they're feeling as part of a general discussion about their mental health and well-being.
- They'll also be asked if they still have any vaginal discharge and whether they have had a period since the birth.
- BP is often checked.
- Mothers may be offered an examination to see if stitches have healed when they have had an episiotomy or Caesarean section.
- If the mother was due for a cervical screening test while pregnant, this should be rescheduled for 12 weeks after the birth.
- Mothers will be asked about contraception.
- If a mother is overweight or obese, with a body mass index (BMI) of 30 or more, they may be weighed. Guidance on healthy eating, physical activity and weight loss will be given if appropriate.

(www.nhs.uk/conditions/baby/support-and-services/your-6-week-postnatal-check/)

The NHS advises mothers to make a list of any questions they'd like to ask in advance to take along to the appointment. They also give the advice shown in Figure 1.36.

Tell your doctor if …

- you're feeling sad or anxious – looking after a baby can sometimes feel overwhelming. Do not feel you have to struggle alone or put on a brave face. It's not a sign that you're a bad mother. You need to get help, as you may have postnatal depression. Your doctor or health visitor can provide help and support.
- you're having trouble holding in your pee or wind, or you're soiling yourself with poo
- having sex is painful
- you're not sure if you have had two doses of the MMR vaccination.

**Figure 1.36** NHS advice to mothers due their '6 week postnatal check' with the GP

## 3.3 The developmental needs of children from birth to five years

In order for them to successfully thrive, develop and grow, children need certain basic development needs to be met by their parents and carers.

### Warmth

Parents and carers must ensure that children are kept warm enough, for example, by providing:

- sufficient indoor and outdoor clothing for all weathers and temperatures
- adequate bedding, central heating or other safe heaters.

### Feeding

It is the responsibility of parents and carers to provide food and drink that contains the right nutrients for the baby/child at each stage of development.

Providing children with regular meals and snacks ensures they have the energy they need to grow, learn and play. Healthy food options should be chosen over less healthy ones, which means making time to shop for, prepare and cook food.

### Love and emotional security

All children need and deserve to be loved and brought up in a supportive, nurturing environment. This is demonstrated when a child's needs are met by a loving parent(s) or carer(s), who have their well-being and best interests at heart, are kind to them, interested in them and happy to devote time to them. They will understand the child's emotions and respond with support and encouragement.

**Good practice**

If there are concerns or queries at any point, parents can contact their midwife, health visitor or GP to ask for help and advice.

They can drop into local clinics, which may be held at a children's centre, GP surgery or a community venue, to speak to somebody from the health visiting team.

For urgent queries that involve the health of a baby, parents should contact their GP, NHS 111 or go to an NHS Walk-in Centre or the nearest accident and emergency (A&E) department as soon as possible.

Feeling loved, wanted and nurtured makes a child feel emotionally secure. Being kept physically secure and safe from harm by trusted adults also creates emotional security.

A child who does not receive love and emotional security might:

- fail to thrive
- be unhappy and experience social and emotional difficulties, both at home and in the wider world, for example, when interacting with their peers at playgroup.

A lack of love and emotional security in the early years can continue to impact on children as they grow up, and the effects may even continue to be felt into adulthood.

**Figure 1.37** Babies and children need love and emotional security to thrive

## Rest/sleep

Ensuring children get enough rest and sleep is crucial to their well-being, learning, growth and development.

While young children should be allowed to rest and sleep whenever they need to do so, good routines are generally very helpful, such as a warm bath, a story and then bedtime at the same time each evening.

It's also important to:

- build in plenty of time for quiet, restful activities after busier or physical ones
- remember that activities that require concentration can also be tiring.

Parents and carers may need to reduce their social life to ensure a child gets enough good-quality rest and sleep.

## Fresh air

Fresh air is good for a child's physical health and well-being.

While it's important to protect their skin from the sun when necessary, being outside in the sun can help raise children's vitamin D levels. This helps the body to absorb calcium, which results in stronger bones.

More time outdoors also promotes more physical activity (see exercise below). But it's important to remember that being outside in nature – around plants and trees for instance – can also be soothing and restful. It's also beneficial for children's eyesight to spend time away from artificial light and screens. Safely exploring the outside, including the natural world, is a vital part of children's learning and development.

Fresh air can help children to feel more energised, improve their mood and help them sleep better. Playing in the garden, going to the park or for a walk are all good examples of ways for children to get fresh air.

## Exercise

The NHS tells us that:

> *Being physically active every day is important for the healthy growth and development of babies, toddlers and pre-schoolers.*

For the 0–5 age group, the NHS says:

> *Activity of any intensity should be encouraged, including light activity and more energetic physical activity.*

(www.nhs.uk/live-well/exercise/physical-activity-guidelines-children-under-five-years/)

Exercise is also good for a child's physical health and well-being – young children are built to be busy and active.

- Enough exercise builds fitness and robustness.
- A lack of exercise can have a very negative effect on health, fitness and development.

Examples of physical exercise include tummy time for babies (playing on their tummies), crawling, going for a walk, running around, dancing, playing on ride on toys and trikes, and playing on a slide or climbing frame. There are many more!

**Figure 1.38** Tummy time has many benefits for growth and development

## Cleanliness/hygiene

Children need clean and appropriately hygienic environments. As their immune systems are less mature, it is much easier for a child to pick up an infection.

- Cleanliness in kitchen areas is especially important (see section 4.3).
- The child must also be bathed daily and kept clean and fresh.
- Their clothing and bedding should be regularly laundered.

## Stimulation

Babies and children need stimulation in order to feel energised and interested in the world. It helps them to learn about the world and to develop their social, intellectual, language and communication skills.

Interaction and play are the key ways in which young children are stimulated. It's crucial for parents and carers to talk and play with babies and children frequently throughout the day.

Providing interesting toys and playthings is also very important, but so are sharing rhymes, singing, stories, games, imaginary play and new experiences, to name just a few. (Also see socialisation and play, below.)

## Routine – bath time, feeding

Routines help young children to feel safe and secure. They also help adults to ensure that all of their care needs can be met effectively every day – for instance:

- Feeding needs to be spread out across the day to ensure that children have the nutrition they need to keep them going.
- Children need a bath every 24 hours – parents often choose to bathe young children every evening then put them into their nightclothes as part of their pre-bed routine.

## Shelter/home

At the most basic level, every child needs shelter/a home – somewhere to stay that will keep them safe and secure whatever the environment and whatever the weather. This will allow their other basic needs – such as safe and sufficient sleep and a clean and hygienic environment – to be fully met.

Parents and carers should ensure the home is healthy for children to live in (e.g. it is not damp, as this can cause asthma/chest infections).

## Socialisation/play

All children need opportunities to play in ways that are appropriate to their stage of development (see Unit R059). Under the UN Convention on the Rights of the Child (UNCRC), all children have a fundamental right to play.

It's very important that children socialise with their peers, and play is the perfect way to achieve this:

- Children learn how to interact with others and form relationships through their play, allowing them to develop qualities such as empathy and fairness.

- Socialising with adults outside the family home is also important – for instance, with wider family members, with staff, volunteers or other parents at childcare centres, nurseries and parent and toddler groups.

## Opportunities for listening and talking

Listening and talking with a child shows that you care about them and are interested in them.

- This is very important to their social and emotional development.
- It is also vital for their intellectual and language development – just think of all the things a child learns in conversation.

**Figure 1.39** Listening and talking with a child shows that you care about them

## Acceptable patterns of behaviour

Children need to learn how to behave in socially acceptable ways, and adults should always strive to be positive role models for children.

Adults also need to have a consistent approach to discipline, or a child may become confused, unsure or even worried about the reaction their behaviour will cause.

### Need for boundaries

Children need to be aware of the boundaries set for their behaviour. In other words, they need to know what they can and cannot do.

Boundaries should also be consistent – it is unfair to send a child mixed messages.

By always explaining why a particular behaviour is unacceptable, you can help a child to think through a situation. Then they will begin to moderate their own behaviour in similar situations in future.

*Promoting positive behaviour*

This is by far the best way to limit inappropriate behaviour. When adults notice and praise specific positive behaviour, a child tends to feel proud of themselves, and they enjoy the approval they receive. This encourages them to repeat the socially acceptable behaviour, until it becomes an ingrained, normal part of what they do.

Verbal praise is the most effective form of praise, and the easiest to give.

If there is a behaviour goal in place for a child, a reward chart can also be an effective visual reward system – see the case study here for an example.

## Case study

Three-year-old Darius has been having tantrums at bedtime most nights for the past three weeks. His auntie, whom he lives with, has made a sticker chart to try and help Darius settle down for sleep appropriately.

She has shown him the chart, which features a picture of a space rocket, one of Darius's favourite things. Each time he goes to bed without a fuss, Darius will be given a sticker to put on the rocket. They talk about how wonderful the rocket will look when all of the stickers have been collected.

Within a few days, Darius has received three stickers. By the second week, he receives a sticker for five days out of seven.

1 Why do you think Darius's behaviour is changing?
2 What other sorts of behaviour do you think might be improved with the use of a sticker chart?
3 Can you suggest other ways in which positive behaviour could be promoted in this scenario?

## Practice question

Couple Daniel and Melanie have brought their new baby home from the hospital. The midwife has advised them to establish a routine.

State the benefits of a routine for bath time and feeding. [2 marks]

## Topic area 4 Childhood illnesses and a child-safe environment

## Getting started

Think back to when you were young. Working with a partner, discuss a childhood illness that you had, such as chickenpox. Talk about how you felt physically (e.g. itchy and tired) and emotionally (e.g. upset to miss out on activities with friends). Now swap roles and listen to your partner.

## 4.1 Recognise general signs and symptoms of illness in children

### Key signs and symptoms of illness

Learning how to recognise, manage and prevent childhood illnesses is a vital part of keeping children safe.

Babies and younger children in particular do not have the language to tell you when something is wrong and they are feeling poorly, so knowing the signs and symptoms of illness is important.

Illnesses can become progressively worse and even threaten lives if they are not quickly treated, so you need to know what to do if a child becomes ill in your care.

To successfully recognise and treat common childhood ailments and diseases, you need to know about:

- general signs of illness
- common childhood ailments and diseases
- caring for a sick child
- when to seek treatment from a doctor
- when to seek emergency medical help.

Children might display the following signs and symptoms of illness:

- vomiting and diarrhoea
- high temperature
- tiredness/disturbed sleep
- reduced appetite
- flushed or pale complexion/lip area
- irritable/fretful behaviour
- lack of desire to play
- headache
- swollen glands
- runny/blocked-up nose
- cough.

You will often see two or more of these signs together. For instance, a child coming down with a cold may have a blocked-up nose, a cough and a reduced appetite.

A child displaying any of these symptoms will need monitoring and sympathetic care.

Signs, symptoms and treatments of specific illnesses are given in Table 1.3 (and see the next section for information on meningitis). You'll learn more about meeting the needs of a sick child in section 4.2.

## Activity

Read through Table 1.3 of childhood illnesses carefully.
Working in threes:

- One student reads out a specific illness from the table, along with its symptoms.
- The other two students, working together, can suggest the appropriate treatment.

**Table 1.3** Childhood ailments and illnesses

| Illness | Spread | Signs and symptoms | Rash or specific sign | Treatment |
|---|---|---|---|---|
| Mumps | Airborne/droplet<br>Incubation 14–21 days | Pain, swelling of the jaw in front of ears, fever, eating and drinking is painful | Swollen face | Fluids given via a straw (if child is old enough to manage this), hot compresses, oral hygiene |
| Measles | Airborne/droplet<br>Incubation 7–15 days | High fever, fretful, heavy cold – running nose and discharge from eyes, a cough later | Day 1: Koplik's spots (clustered white legions inside of mouth)<br>Day 4: blotchy rash begins to spread on face and body | Rest, fluids, tepid sponging, shaded room if light is uncomfortable to eyes |
| Tonsillitis | Direct infection, droplet | Very sore throat, fever, headache, pain on swallowing, aches and pains in back and limbs | | Rest, fluid, medical aid, antibiotics, iced drinks to relieve the pain |
| Chickenpox | Airborne/droplet, direct contact<br>Incubation 10–14 days | Slight fever, itchy rash, mild onset then child feels ill, often with severe headache | Red spots with a white centre on trunk and limbs at first, blisters and pustules | Rest, fluids, calamine lotion on rash, cut child's nails to prevent secondary infection from scratching |
| Common cold | Airborne/droplet, hand-to-hand contact<br>Incubation 1–3 days | Sore throat, sneezing, running nose, headache, slight fever, irritability, partial deafness | | Treat symptoms |
| Gastroenteritis | Direct contact: incubation 7–14 days<br>Indirect: infected food or drink, incubation 30 minutes–36 hours | Vomiting and diarrhoea, signs of dehydration | | Replace fluids – water (or rehydrating remedy), seek urgent medical aid |
| Meningitis | Airborne/droplet<br>Incubation 2–10 days | High fever, vomiting, headache, stiff neck, drowsiness, confusion, dislike of bright lights, seizures | Red/purple spots that do not fade when the side of a glass is pressed against them | Antibiotics, fluids, oxygen if necessary, steroid medication, seek treatment in hospital |

## Key signs and symptoms of when to seek emergency medical help

The following section provides information on emergency situations in which you will need to act calmly and quickly. This includes the signs and symptoms of meningitis.

The following signs and symptoms of illness indicate that you need to call for urgent medical attention – i.e. that you need to call an ambulance:

- breathing difficulties (also see section on asthma below)
- child is unresponsive – cannot easily or fully be roused from sleep, or a state of drowsiness
- baby becomes unresponsive and/or their body seems to be floppy or limp
- high fever/temperature that cannot be lowered (see below)
- seizures/fitting (see below)

### *Meningitis*

A child with meningitis may have the following symptoms:

- a high temperature or fever
- vomiting
- severe headache
- stiff neck
- drowsiness
- confusion
- dislike of bright lights
- seizures (fitting)
- a skin rash of red/purple 'pinprick' spots.

If the spots spread they can resemble fresh bruising, but this is hard to see on black skin. The rash will not fade when the side of a glass is pressed against it. In babies, there may also be restlessness and a high-pitched crying or screaming, a limp or floppy body, swelling of the fontanelle area of the skull (the soft spot on the top of the head) and refusal to feed.

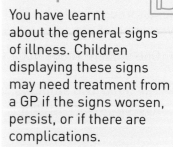

**Good practice**

You have learnt about the general signs of illness. Children displaying these signs may need treatment from a GP if the signs worsen, persist, or if there are complications.

You should always be cautious with children's health, and if you are worried, it is far better to call the doctor or the NHS advice line 111 for advice than to delay.

A doctor must be called immediately, because meningitis can be life-threatening, and the child might deteriorate quickly. If a doctor cannot be contacted or is delayed, call 999 (or 112 from a mobile) for an ambulance. Do not wait for all of the symptoms to appear. If a child has already seen a doctor but is becoming worse, seek urgent medical attention again. Reassure the child and keep them cool until help arrives.

**Good practice**
You can download a free app that will tell you all you need to know about meningitis. It has saved lives, because people can check the symptoms instantly if they are concerned about a child. You can download the app here:

**www.meningitisnow.org/ meningitis-explained/ signs-and-symptoms/ download-our-mobile-app/**

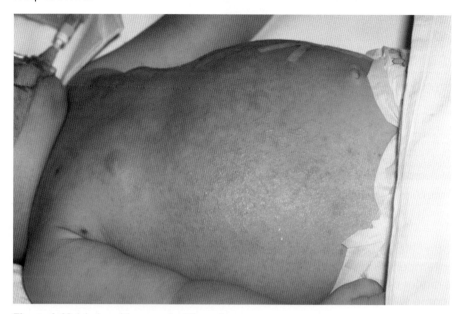

**Figure 1.40** A baby with a meningitis rash

## Breathing difficulties

Breathing difficulties may occur after contact with allergens such as dust, pollen or pet hair, and can also be caused by the child having a cold, experiencing stress or extreme cold. The child may cough, wheeze and become breathless.

If a child is known to be asthmatic, they should have a 'reliever' inhaler immediately available. These are generally blue, and deliver medication to the lungs to relieve affected airways. Reassure and give the inhaler as instructed. Make sure you know which inhaler to use in an emergency.

How to support the child with breathing difficulties:

● Sit the child upright and leaning forwards in a comfortable position – they should never lie down.
● Stay with them.
● If the breathing difficulties don't improve, persists or worsens, call for an ambulance.

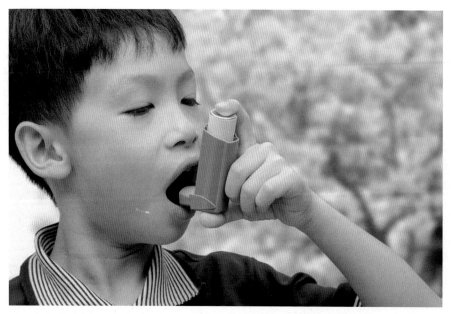

**Figure 1.41** A 'reliever' inhaler delivers medication to the lungs

### High temperatures

The normal temperature reading for a child is between 36.5 °C and 37.4 °C. Children may have a higher temperature when they are ill. Taking a child's temperature with a digital or scan thermometer helps you to monitor their illness. These come with directions for use.

You should take steps to lower a temperature by:

- ensuring that warm clothing is removed so that just a cool layer is worn
- providing a cool drink, either water or another drink diluted with water.

Some children may be given paracetamol syrup by parents or carers (e.g. if a child is prone to convulsions brought on by a high temperature).

### Seizures/fitting

Seizures/fitting may be due to epilepsy or a high temperature. There may be violent muscle twitching, clenched fists and an arched back, which may lead to unconsciousness.

- Call an ambulance.
- Instead of trying to restrain the child, clear the immediate area and surround the child with pillows or padding for protection.
- Cool the child gradually (as for a temperature, see above).
- If the seizure stops before help arrives, place the child in the recovery position. You will learn how to place a casualty in the recovery position if you take a first aid course.

**Test your knowledge**

1 What are the common signs of illness?
2 When would you seek emergency treatment for a child?
3 Make a list of the signs and symptoms of meningitis

## 4.2 How to meet the needs of an ill child

When a child is unwell, they rely on adults to meet all of their needs. These fall into four categories:

- physical needs
- social needs
- emotional needs
- intellectual needs.

### *Physical needs*

- When a child is sick, they need plenty of rest, so you will need to adjust their usual routines to allow for extra naps, particularly if night-time sleep has been disturbed (e.g. through coughing or vomiting).

- You will also need to adjust their diet, if they have an upset stomach, for example. But it is always important to ensure that plenty of water (or diluted juice) is taken.

- Always monitor a sick child carefully, as conditions can worsen suddenly, and be ready to call for medical help if necessary.

- Make sure that you are aware of a child's medical conditions (such as asthma or diabetes) and that you know what to do if there is a problem.

- High temperatures or fevers are often seen in young children, so you should know how to care for a child experiencing these (see section 4.1).

**Figure 1.42** If a child is feeling unwell, they need plenty of rest

## Social and emotional needs

An ill child needs empathy and plenty of reassurance, especially when they are too young to understand how they feel. It can be confusing and frightening to suddenly feel unwell.

Adults should gently explain the illness to a child, and if appropriate, let them know that they will feel better soon. Talking positively about any medication; naps and healthy eating can also help.

Children's desire to have company might be just as strong as ever, so activities you can do together are especially helpful.

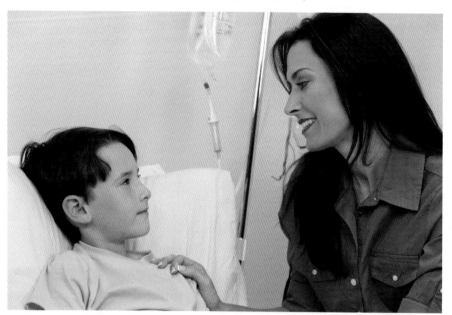

**Figure 1.43** Adults should gently explain the illness to a child

## Intellectual needs

Children are likely to need quiet activities to keep them amused and stimulated while they are not up to more active play. Stories, colouring activities and IT devices are popular choices.

If a child is ill or will be recovering for a longer period, it will be important to think carefully about activities that will help their learning and development to continue as expected. If appropriate, visits from friends and family will also be beneficial, as children can miss wider social contact.

---

### Test your knowledge

1 Suggest some ways in which you could meet the intellectual needs of an ill child.

---

**Good practice**

**Good practice**

Children might need extra physical affection, such as cuddles or sitting on your lap. Also bear in mind that for a short time, an ill child might also regress in their behaviour, going back to things they did that brought them comfort when they were younger, such as clinging to an adult's legs or sucking their thumb.

## 4.3 How to ensure a child-friendly safe environment

For anyone looking after a child, the most crucial responsibility is to keep that child safe from harm. When asked, most parents will say that their biggest hope for their children is that they will be 'safe and happy'.

Whether a child is safe and happy also tends to be a parent's main concern when they leave them in the care of someone else. So it is vital that you know:

- how to maintain a safe environment for children
- how to provide safe equipment
- about the most common childhood accidents, and issues relating to social and internet safety.

### What a hazard is

A **hazard** is an item or situation that could cause harm to a child, and potential hazards are all around us. They include:

- physical hazards – such as unsafe objects; things that may be tripped over
- security hazards – such as insecure exits and windows
- fire hazards – such as heaters and electrical appliances
- food safety hazards – such as a faulty refrigerator; unsafe produce
- personal safety hazards – such as stranger danger; busy roads.

A **risk** is the likelihood of the hazard actually causing harm. For example, whenever we walk along the pavement, road traffic – a significant potential hazard – is very close to us. But the likelihood of actually being harmed by traffic in this situation is low.

**Key terms**

**Hazard** A hazard is an item or situation that could cause harm to a child.

**Risk** The likelihood of a hazard actually causing harm.

**Activity**

Choose one of the following rooms:

- kitchen  - bathroom  - living room  - bedroom.

Now think about possible risks to a young child's safety that might be present in that room in your own home. Thought storm as many as you can think of (e.g. there might be bleach in the bathroom).

**Figure 1.44** Environments should be as safe as possible

## Good practice

Young children need adults to make the environments in which they spend their time as safe as possible. This means identifying the hazards in the environment. To do this:

● Think carefully about a particular space, and identify all of the apparent hazards in that space.
● Take steps to reduce the possibility of the hazard causing harm to an acceptable level.

There will always be accidents, as children cannot be wrapped up in cotton wool. But you can do your best to protect children from foreseeable accidents.

## Recognise common hazards and how these can be prevented

### *Within the home*

Most accidents occur at home. When thinking about safety, it is best to consider each room or area at a time:

- kitchen
- toilet/bathroom
- stairs
- play areas/gardens.

You need to think carefully about child development when you are addressing hazards. This will help you to:

- consider how aware children are of danger at various ages
- think about their skill levels, and the things they are likely to do – for example, a 12-month-old is likely to pull themselves up on a chair, which might be unsafe. They could also open low kitchen cupboards when sitting on the floor.

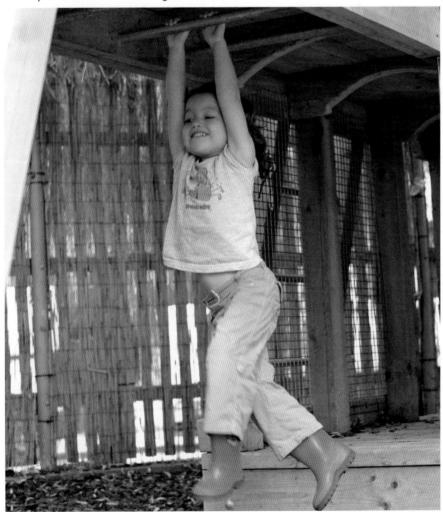

**Figure 1.45** Play equipment must be age-appropriate

Table 1.4 lists the likely hazards for each room/area.

**Table 1.4** Possible hazards in the kitchen, toilet/bathroom, stairs, play areas and garden

| Area | Hazards are likely to include ... |
|---|---|
| *Kitchen* | • unsafe chemicals children could handle, e.g. cleaning products, dishwasher tablets, washing powder<br>• food safety hazards, e.g. raw meat<br>• dangerously hot equipment, e.g. oven, grill, hob, microwave, toaster, kettle, coffee maker (and hot items that are/have been in them, e.g. food, water)<br>• sharp equipment, e.g. knives, skewers, scissors, tin openers, graters<br>• fragile items that become dangerous when broken, e.g. crockery, glasses<br>• electronic food preparation equipment, e.g. blenders, tin openers, food processors, juicers<br>• access to power sockets<br>• access to hot taps<br>• access to water (drowning risk)<br>• a window from which a child could fall |
| *Toilet/ bathroom* | • unsafe chemicals for children to handle, e.g. cleaning products, bleach, medicines, toiletries<br>• sharp equipment, e.g. razors<br>• access to hot taps and hot water<br>• access to water (drowning risk)<br>• access to items unhygienic for children to handle, e.g. toilet brush, inside of the toilet<br>• access to items that are slippery when wet, e.g. bath, shower tray, floor<br>• a window from which a child could fall |
| *Stairs* | • items left on the stairs that could be tripped over<br>• risk of tripping<br>• risk of falling<br>• faulty or missing handrail |
| *Play areas/ garden* | • insecure gates, sheds or boundary fences<br>• possibility of strangers or animals coming into contact with children<br>• problems caused by weather, e.g. icy patches or waterlogged areas<br>• not enough shelter or protection from the sun<br>• other risks from water, e.g. ponds, water courses or gullies<br>• open litter bins and drains<br>• litter, glass, poisonous plants and animal faeces (cats are particularly attracted to an uncovered sand tray)<br>• items/equipment that could cause harm<br>• play equipment which is not assembled safely and/or is not age-appropriate<br>• unsafe flooring – mats might be needed under play equipment |

## *Roads*

Road safety is extremely important. Young children should always be under close and direct supervision of adults when walking on the pavement or crossing the road.

If you are in charge of a child who is old enough to be walking near a road, you should hold their hand at all times. Follow the five point Green Cross Code and make children aware of it:

1 **First find the safest place to cross.**
   - If possible, cross the road at: subways; footbridges; islands; zebra, puffin, pelican or toucan crossings; or where there is a crossing point controlled by a police officer, a school crossing patrol or a traffic warden.
   - Otherwise, choose a place where you can see clearly in all directions, and where drivers can see you.
   - Try to avoid crossing between parked cars and on sharp bends or close to the top of a hill. Move to a space where drivers and riders can see you clearly.
   - There should be space to reach the pavement on the other side.

2 **Stop just before you get to the kerb.**
   - Do not get too close to the traffic. If there is no pavement, keep back from the edge of the road but make sure you can still see approaching traffic.
   - Give yourself lots of time to have a good look all around.

3 **Look all around for traffic and listen.**
   - Look in every direction.
   - Listen carefully, because you can sometimes hear traffic before you can see it.

4 **If traffic is coming, let it pass.**
   - Look all around again and listen.
   - Do not cross until there is a safe gap in the traffic and you are certain that there is plenty of time.
   - Remember, even if traffic is a long way off, it may be approaching very quickly.

5 **When it is safe, go straight across the road – do not run.**
   - Keep looking and listening for traffic while you cross, in case there is any traffic you did not see, or in case other traffic appears suddenly.
   - Look out for cyclists and motorcyclists travelling between lanes of traffic.
   - Do not cross diagonally.
   - When out walking, toddlers are safest on reins, and babies and children in prams or buggies should wear a harness.

## Activity

1 Find out more about road safety by visiting this website: **www.think.gov.uk/education-resources/**

Explore the resources for 3–6 year olds, and read the information given.

2 Now write down five things you will do to promote road safety when working with young children.

## Preventing hazards

Table 1.5 shows key safety equipment that can prevent accidents.

**Table 1.5** Key safety equipment. Can you think of additional safety measures you can take to protect children from harm?

| Equipment | Purpose |
|---|---|
| Harness and reins | Prevent falls from prams, push chairs and high chairs. Prevent young children escaping and/or running into the road when out walking. |
| Safety gates | Prevent access to kitchens, stairways, outdoors. Always place a guard at the bottom and top of stairs for babies and young children. |
| Locks for cupboards and windows | Prevent children getting hold of dangerous substances or falling from windows. |
| Safety glass/safety film | Prevent glass from breaking into pieces, causing injuries. |
| Socket covers | Prevent children from poking their fingers into electrical sockets. |
| Play pens | Create a safe area for babies. |
| Smoke alarms | Detect smoke and sound the alarm. |
| Cooker guards | Prevent children pulling pans from the cooker. |
| Firefighting equipment such as a fire blankets or extinguishers | May be used to tackle minor fires. |

## The importance of safety labelling

Safety labelling tells you whether a product or piece of equipment is safe for use by children. Any relevant additional safety information will be specified: see Table 1.6 for an explanation of safety labelling.

You must always check for safety marks and read safety information before buying or using products for children.

**Table 1.6** Safety labelling

| Safety mark | | Explanation |
|---|---|---|
| BSI Kitemark™ | **Figure 1.46** BSI Kitemark™ | The BSI Kitemark™ is a UK product and service quality certification mark, administered by the British Standards Institution (BSI). <br> • It is used to identify products where safety is paramount, e.g. bicycle helmets and smoke alarms. <br> • It gives assurance that the product should be safe and reliable, but manufacturers are not legally required to display a Kitemark™ on their products. |
| Lion mark | **Figure 1.47** Lion Mark | The Lion Mark was developed by the British Toy and Hobby Association (BTHA) which supply around 90 per cent of toys sold in the UK. <br> It was developed in 1988 to act as a recognisable consumer symbol denoting safety and quality. |
| CE symbol, UKCA mark and UKNI mark | **Figure 1.48** CE symbol <br> **Figure 1.49** UKCA mark <br> **Figure 1.50** UKNI mark | The CE symbol was previously the most common toy label and the first one to look for. By law, it has to be displayed on all new toys on the market in the EU. The CE logo proves that the toy has been tested for compliance with EU standards. It is also the manufacturer's declaration that the item meets all toy safety requirements. <br> The CE symbol is being phased out in Great Britain and replaced by the UKCA mark and the UKNI symbol in Northern Ireland. From January 2023, only the UKCA mark will be given to eligible products. <br> However, you will find for some time that products on the shelf still carry the CE mark, until old stock of these items sell out and are refreshed with newer stock issued with the UKCA mark. |

**Table 1.6** Safety labelling (continued)

| Safety mark | | Explanation |
|---|---|---|
| Age advice symbol | **Figure 1.51** Age advice symbol | This symbol identifies when equipment or a product isn't suitable for children under the age of 36 months (in the opinion of the manufacturer).<br><br>• It is mainly displayed on toys that might not pass a 'choke hazard test'.<br>• It is also seen if a product has small parts that could be removed and swallowed by children under three years. |
| Children's nightwear labelling | Nightwear can burn quickly if set alight by contact with an open fire, gas or electric fire, or another heat source, and this can cause serious injury.<br><br>As a result, you should look for a label confirming that children's night garments (including dressing gowns) meet the flammability performance requirements. This includes garments for babies. | |

## Good practice

Stretch garments such as baby grows should be treated as children's nightwear.

## Test your knowledge

1 Write down the measures you would take to keep a child safe in the kitchen.
2 Write down the measures you would take to keep a child safe in the bathroom.
3 List some safety labels and say why each one is important.

## Practice question

Identify the safety label shown here, then state the meaning of the mark and why it is used on specific products.  [3 marks]

## Read about it

### Weblinks

A guide to the health of women before and during pregnancy (Read the section on women's health before pregnancy. Women's health during pregnancy isn't relevant to this unit.):

https://assets.publishing.service.gov.uk/government/uploads/system/uploads/attachment_data/file/844210/Health_of_women_before_and_during_pregnancy_2019.pdf

Read about fertility on this Fertility UK webpage:

www.fertilityuk.org/page1

The Child-to-Child Trust's *Caring for Children who are Sick*:

www.childtochild.org.uk/wp-content/uploads/2015/12/AS-6.2-Caring-for-children-who-are-sick.pdf

### Reference books

Read about conception and the development of the embryo and foetus, and see photos of this development inside the uterus:

*Dynamic Risk Management in the Early Years* (Early Years Alliance, 2017)

*Good Practice in Early Years Infection Control* (Early Years Alliance, 2009)

Meggitt, Carolyn, *Understand Child Development* (Teach Yourself, 2012)

Nilsson, Lennart and Forsell, Linda (2020) *A Child Is Born*, 5th edition, Random House Publishing.

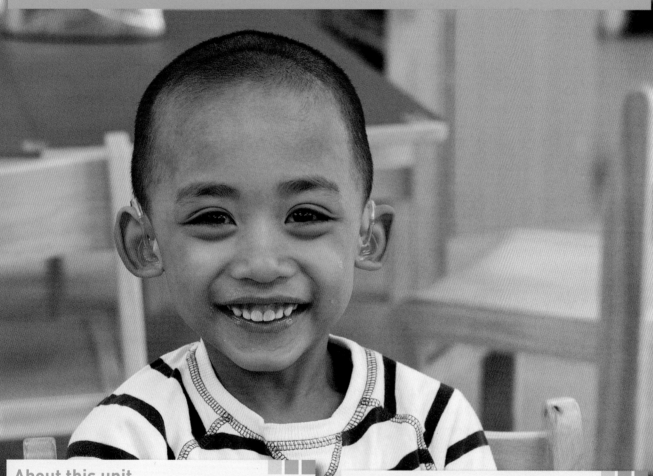

# Create a safe environment and understand the nutritional needs of children from birth to five years

## About this unit

In this unit you will learn about the importance of creating a safe environment for children in a childcare setting. This includes how to choose appropriate equipment for the setting, which is quite different to providing equipment for a child within the home setting. You'll also learn about the nutritional needs of children from birth to five years.

## Topic areas

In this unit you will learn about:

1 Creating a safe environment in a childcare setting
2 Choosing suitable equipment for a childcare setting
3 Nutritional needs of children from birth to five years

**How will I be assessed?**

You will complete a set assignment that contains four practical tasks. This will be assessed by your Centre and moderated later by OCR.

## Topic area 1 Creating a safe environment in a childcare setting

**Getting started**

Think back to when you were young. Working with a partner, discuss a childhood accident that you had (such as falling off your bike). Talk about how you felt physically (in pain perhaps). Now swap over and listen to your partner.

## 1.1 Plan to create a safe environment in a childcare setting

Everyone who works with children must always do their best to prevent accidents, injuries and illnesses. Because of this, it's important to understand the reasons why accidents happen. You can consider the potential risks and take preventative action when appropriate.

### Reasons why accidents happen in a childcare setting

#### The environment

All children experience minor accidents. Childcare settings are busy environments:

- Compared to the home, simply having more children on the premises naturally means there will be a higher incidence of accidents.
- In a childcare setting, children tend to have more space for physical play and access to more large play equipment (e.g. climbing frames) than at home, which may lead to accidents.
- They may also have more access to liquids (e.g. pouring their own drinks, water play), leading to more spillages and potential slips.
- Children will be learning new skills and playing in new ways for the first time (e.g. using ride on toys, and playing playground games).
- Children may engage in 'rough and tumble' play with peers from time to time.

**Figure 2.1** Young children access large play equipment in childcare settings

## Lack of supervision

In most cases there will be a higher ratio of adults to children in the home than there will be in a childcare setting. For instance, a parent may supervise just two children aged three to five years at home, while at a childcare setting there may be one practitioner for every eight children aged three to five years.

But when a group childcare setting observes best practice, lack of supervision should not be a problem. Dedicated staff will solely look after children; they won't have the same demands on their time as a parent at home (e.g. cleaning the house, cooking meals, laundry etc). But problems do occur if:

- the number of staff is insufficient
- time management is lacking
- staff are not effectively deployed, including a lack of close supervision for activities which require this (e.g. cooking or using tools)
- staff have not been appropriately trained, whether for the age range or the environment
- untrained, or new, staff are not closely monitored.

## Untrained staff

Poor safety practice can be down to a lack of staff training. It's very important for childcare settings to follow the rules and ensure that there is always the correct number of trained staff at every session.

**Good practice**

In a positive example of supervision, a member of staff may lead story time with a large group of young children, while one colleague sets up a craft activity nearby in the same room, and another sets up the water tray outside. Story time is a low-risk activity and there is a colleague on hand if any assistance is needed with the children.

However, supervision would not be so effective if one member of staff then took the large group of children outside by themselves, and attempted to supervise them all during physical play with large equipment.

## Safety equipment

In childcare settings, failing to use, check or adjust safety equipment to meet the needs of an individual child can be problematic. For instance:

- Safety reins must be adjusted to fit each toddler before taking them for a walk outside of the setting.

The safety straps on a highchair will need to be adjusted to fit each child that sits in it.

Without these measures, the safety equipment will not be fully operational.

## As part of a child's development

See R057 for information on how it is natural for children to have some minor accidents as part of their development. When all other safety standards are met, the overall environment supports children's developmental stage.

This is especially true as young children become more curious and mobile. For instance, a curious baby who has just learnt to crawl may now be able to open cupboards and turn out the contents, or to access and touch electrical wall sockets. This means that child cupboard locks, stair gates and socket covers should be fitted, where appropriate, within the childcare setting. A toddler who is learning to walk will pull themselves up on furniture, stumble and fall on many occasions. It is important that 'safety corners' are applied to pointed tables and there are no trip hazards to minimise the likelihood of the toddler hurting themselves within the childcare setting.

## Types of childhood accidents

The most common childhood accidents are shown in Figure 2.2.

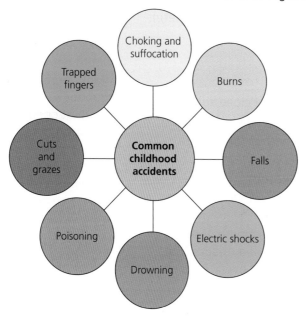

**Figure 2.2** Common childhood accidents. Would you know how to respond to these?

> **Good practice**
>
> To prevent choking:
>
> - keep small objects out of reach
> - check and follow the age recommendations on toys
> - keep toys for small children and older children separately
> - ensure children sit up when eating, keep food pieces small and encourage them to chew food well.
>
> To prevent suffocation:
>
> - follow safe sleeping guidelines (see Unit R057)
> - keep plastic bags (including nappy sacks) well out of reach of babies and children
> - avoid garments that could catch around a child's neck such as scarves.

## Choking and suffocation

Babies and children can choke to death on any small object they put in their mouths that blocks their airway, so you must be very careful which objects are left within reach.

In addition, children can struggle to breathe or stop breathing due to suffocation. This can happen when the airway is blocked externally, for example:

- if a child puts their head into a plastic bag
- if something heavy falls on their chest
- if an item (such as a scarf) gets caught around their neck.

Choking on food is also common, and can be caused in a number of ways:

- laughing or gasping when eating
- trying to swallow a piece of food that is too large
- eating lying down.

## Burns

The causes of burns and scalds are shown in Figure 2.3. Scalds are caused by liquids – the majority of scalds are caused by hot drinks or hot water.

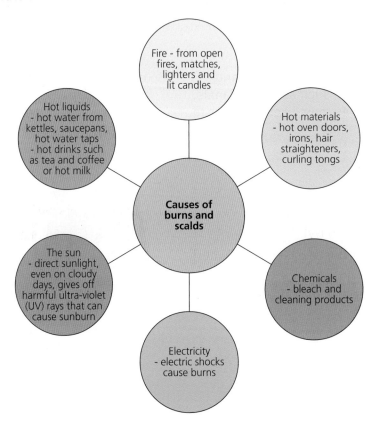

**Figure 2.3** The causes of burns and scalds. Are there any chemicals in your home that could scald a child?

**Synoptic link**

This topic area has links to Unit R057, specifically section 4.3.

**Good practice**

To prevent burns and scalds:

- use a kettle with a short cord to stop it hanging over the edge of the work surface, where it could be grabbed
- when cooking, use the rings at the back of the cooker and turn saucepan handles towards the back so they cannot be grabbed
- put cold water into a bath first, then add the hot water and test the temperature before putting a baby or child in the bath
- fit fireguards to all fires and heaters
- keep hot drinks well away from young children
- cover children up with a t-shirt and hat, and use sunscreen to prevent sunburn.

## Falls

Falls are a very common form of injury in childhood. Causes of a fall include:

- lack of balance when learning to walk
- lack of experience and co-ordination when playing on equipment such as climbing frames, slides and roundabouts
- tripping and falling down stairs or out of windows
- falling from changing tables, beds or sofas.

## Electric shocks

Electricity can be extremely dangerous, and electric shocks can kill by stopping the heart. Electric shocks can be caused by children poking fingers or objects into electric sockets.

- If a child has been electrocuted, it is vital to stop the flow of electricity. Do not approach the child until the electricity has been switched off, otherwise you are also likely to receive an electric shock.
- Turn the power off at the mains or master switch. If this isn't possible, push or pull the child well away from the source using material that will not conduct electricity.
- Techniques could include looping a thick towel around the child's feet so that you can pull them, or using a wooden broom to push them away from the electricity source.

## Drowning

Drowning can occur in natural water bodies such as the sea and rivers. It can also occur in man-made places, such as pools, canals, lakes, ponds and baths. These are the places most likely to occur to you when you think about the risk of drowning.

## Poisoning

Poisons enter the body when they:

- are swallowed (e.g. medication, bleach or berries)
- come into contact with the skin (e.g. poison ivy)
- are inhaled (e.g. poisonous gas fumes or dust such as ant powder).

Some common household/workplace substances and plants can poison children, and it is important to guard against this. Common items that can poison include:

- cleaning fluids and sprays
- medication, including over-the-counter medication and prescription drugs
- personal care products and make-up
- pesticides (which should never be used around children)

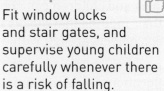

**Good practice**
Fit window locks and stair gates, and supervise young children carefully whenever there is a risk of falling.

**Good practice**
It is important to fit socket covers that protect children from electric shocks. In purpose build childcare settings, many sockets are positioned out of the reach of children, and socket covers will also be used.

**Good practice**
Never leave a baby or young child unattended anywhere near water, even for a few seconds. This includes in the bath or paddling pool.

**Figure 2.4** Cleaning fluids can cause poisoning

- some plants including delphinium, mistletoe (including berries), wild mushrooms and other fungi, foxgloves, daffodil bulbs, poison ivy. Berries from bushes and trees should all be regarded as poisonous because it is difficult to tell which are which.

## *Cuts and grazes*

However careful and safety aware parents and carers are, all children get cuts and grazes as part of their development.

For instance, young children are particularly prone to cuts, grazes, bumps and bruises as they often trip and fall as they learn how to walk.

Later, the same is true when they learn to run, climb, slide, ride a bike and so on. Even older children will hurt themselves while playing or taking part in sports.

Most cuts and grazes are minor, can be treated by parents and carers and will heal in a few days. However, they can be sore at the time, and young children often cry and need comforting when they sustain a cut or graze out of the blue.

## *Trapped fingers*

According to the Royal Society for the Prevention of Accidents (RoSPA), about 30,000 children trap their fingers in doors each year, and more than 1500 of them need surgery. Injuries from self-shutting fire safety doors, car doors and hinges are particularly common.

## Plan to prevent accidents in a childcare setting

To promote safety, it's important to consider how to prevent accidents when planning activities in a childcare setting. The diagram in Figure 2.5 shows how accidents can be prevented. Read this carefully.

**Good practice**

Keep items that could poison out of children's reach, ideally in a locked cupboard. Do not introduce plants to a setting unless they can be identified as safe.

**Good practice**

Use playground safety flooring under play equipment, and non-slip flooring inside.

**Good practice**

Use small C-shaped devices made of foam or rubber over doors to prevent them slamming (but these are not suitable for fire doors). Hinge protectors can also be fitted on most doors.

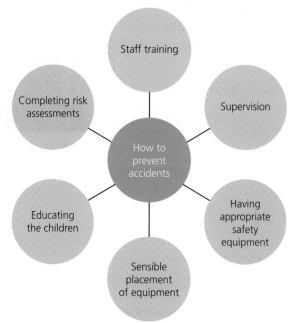

**Figure 2.5** How accidents can be prevented

## Different areas in a childcare setting

A childcare setting is divided into different areas or zones. Some key areas are permanent fixtures – this means they remain in the same place at every session. These areas generally include:

- sleep areas
- mealtime and snack time areas
- food preparation areas
- toileting and changing areas
- book corner
- imaginary area (e.g. home corner)
- outside large equipment area
- messy play area.

Other areas are dedicated to activities on a flexible basis, depending on the activity plans for the day. For example:

- mark making table
- tabletop games
- construction play area
- small world play space
- music zone (with instruments)
- sensory play area
- puppet theatre
- circle time space.

## Having appropriate safety equipment

The prevention of accidents needs to be considered carefully for each area of the setting. This applies to both permanent areas and flexible areas. It's vital to have the appropriate equipment to ensure children's safety, such as:

- a safety gate to prevent children from entering food preparation areas
- stair gates to prevent children from falling down stairs
- safety flooring or mats underneath play equipment
- socket covers on electric sockets
- reins on highchairs
- no small interlocking bricks within the reach of younger children.

Also see 'safety equipment' in section 1.1, and Unit R057 section 4.3.

**Figure 2.6** Stair gates protect young children from falls.

## Placement of equipment in the area

- It's important to consider safety when deciding where to place equipment and safety equipment. For example: climbing frames, slides and most other large playground apparatus must be placed on a flat surface.
- The surface should also be safe. For example: there may be safety flooring underneath, or safety mats may be used.
- When planning to set out a play activity, it's also important to think about what other children will be doing nearby. For example: it would not be safe to position a mat for babies to lie on outside alongside three year olds playing with balls.

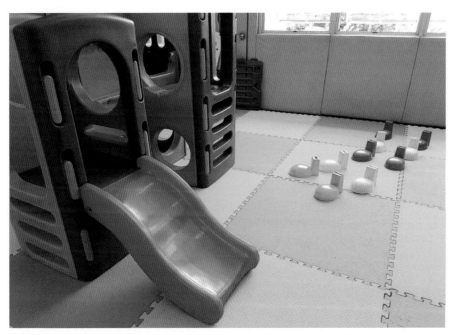

**Figure 2.7** Safety mats can be used around play equipment

## Supervision/Staff requirements for the area

### Supervision

Practitioners must supervise children safely at all times. There are Ofsted rules about the minimum acceptable staff to children ratio. Settings must meet these minimum standards, although many settings aim to exceed them in the interests of quality.

In childcare settings in England (without a qualified teacher), the minimum ratios are:

- children under two years: one adult to three children (1:3)
- children aged two years: one adult to four children (1:4)
- children aged three to seven years: one adult to eight children (1:8).

For safety, staff deployment (the tasks staff undertake) should be carefully considered throughout the session. Generally, the younger the children are, or the more challenging the activity, the closer the supervision will need to be.

- For some activities, children can safely play independently, as long as there are adults in the room keeping a general eye on things – children can approach them if they need assistance.

- Other activities would be unsafe without one-to-one support from an adult – for example, a child learning to use a sharp tool.

Levels of supervision can change as problems occur, the mood of children changes or when children master skills. Practitioners learn through experience to adjust the level of supervision they give accordingly. Also see 'lack of supervision', earlier in this section.

### Staff training

Promoting health and safety is a vital element of a practitioner's role, and it is studied as part of early years qualifications.

It's also very important for childcare providers to train all their staff in how to keep children safe in their own particular setting. This includes ensuring that everyone understands and knows how to follow the setting's health and safety policies and procedures. Also see 'untrained staff', earlier in this section.

### Safety considerations

It's important that no safety considerations are forgotten during a busy childcare session.

You have been learning about ways in which practitioners plan ahead, such as carrying out risk assessments and considering safe supervision of the children. Another way to consider safety is to create a plan for a specific area of the childcare setting.

### Creating a plan for an area of a childcare setting

Creating a plan for an area of a childcare setting helps practitioners to really focus in on the best way to enable children to enjoy specific activities in the space while remaining safe in their play.

Plans can be written. But visual plans showing the proposed layout of an area are also very helpful, especially when there is a considerable time gap between planning an activity and carrying it out (it is easy to forget what was intended), or when the person planning may not be the person setting up the activity on the day. A basic sketch is enough.

**Activity**

On a large sheet of paper, draw the indoor layout plan for a day nursery catering for children aged two to five years. Include the following permanent features:

- sleep area
- mealtime and snack time area
- kitchen (off limits to the children)
- toileting and changing area
- book corner
- home corner
- messy play area.

Leave plenty of space to add flexible areas later.

It can also be extremely helpful to draw a visual plan of the whole play setting, showing where activities will take place during children's free play time. This gives an overhead view. Some settings have printed plans of their playrooms and outside areas on hand, ready for staff to fill in.

### Reasons for plan choices

It's important that good reasoning informs the planning choices you make. You should always aim to offer activities that work well together. Try to avoid creating conflict between activities.

For example:

- You may set up a game of musical sound Lotto at the opposite end of the room from the book corner, because the noise of the game is likely to impact on the quieter and more restful activity of exploring books.
- You may set up a cooking activity not too far away from the door to the bathroom, so children can easily wash their hands before and after, without trailing food stuff throughout the room.

Whole room plans also help practitioners ensure that there aren't too many activities requiring close supervision by staff at the same time.

### Educating the children

Children learn through repetition, and you have probably heard adults remind them of safety rules such as 'Only four children on the climbing frame at once', or 'We don't jump on the bed', or 'Don't touch the radiator'.

Giving a safety instruction and explaining it is an opportunity to educate a child about keeping themselves safe. For example, if a child understands that a crowded climbing frame can be dangerous because everyone needs space to move around safely and not bump into one another or they may fall, they may remember this when they visit the park and wait for crowded apparatus to become less busy before going on.

### Completing risk assessments

An example of preventing accidents is a risk assessment. Most settings will have risk assessment forms for staff to complete before undertaking activities, outings or changes in layout to the setting. Staff will be trained on how to complete the risk assessment.

**Activity**

On the nursery layout plan you made earlier, add eight flexible activity areas of your choosing. Carefully consider where the best place is for these.

Now find a partner. Share your plan and explain the reasons for your choices.

**Test your knowledge**

1 Explain how to prevent burns.
2 Explain how to protect against falls.

## Topic area 2 Choosing suitable equipment for a childcare setting

### Getting started

How much equipment do you think a baby needs? Choose one of the following categories and thought storm as many items as you can think of for the category:

- travelling equipment (for when travelling with the baby on foot, by car and on public transport)
- sleeping equipment
- feeding equipment
- changing equipment
- indoor and outdoor playing (e.g. climbing frame, painting resources).

Children need a range of equipment. For their well-being and safety, it's important that the items selected by a childcare setting are age and weight appropriate and safe.

### Synoptic link

This area has links to the developmental needs of children from birth to five years, covered in Unit R057, specifically section 3.3.

## 2.1 Essential equipment and factors for choice

### Equipment for babies and children from birth to five years

Between birth and the age of 12 months, babies develop and grow faster than any other time in their lives. Between one and five years, children progress from taking their first steps, to running, jumping, peddling and climbing.

Childcare professionals need to provide appropriate equipment at each stage of development, always meeting the child's needs at the right moment in time. A good understanding of child development will help the childcare professional to plan accordingly. You will learn about child development in Unit R059.

Factors affecting suitability and choice:

- Age and weight appropriateness - recommended age ranges for products, maximum and minimum weight recommendations for products
- Safety – safety features, star ratings, safety labelling
- Design – comfort, accessibility, ease of use, aesthetics, adjustability
- Durability – hard wearing, materials
- Cost – value for money, price range

Let's look at each of these in turn.

## Travelling equipment

### Prams and buggies

Some childcare professionals choose to use a pram for newborns and very young babies. Prams allows babies to lie flat and often have a bassinet that can be removed. Prams can be used up to when the baby is about 6 months old. At this point, the baby has the strength to support its own head and can switch to using a buggy.

Others choose an adjustable buggy that can be used throughout the first year and beyond. These have a fully reclining element designed for the younger baby. In most adjustable designs, the buggy can also be manoeuvred to become:

- parent/carer-facing – allows a close eye to be kept on a younger baby, and also enables eye contact and interaction
- outward-facing – allows an older baby to look out into the world.

From the age of around two and a half years, many childcare professionals choose to switch to using a stroller-style buggy or pushchair. This is much lighter weight, making it easier to fold and to pack away when not in use, or when going on a journey.

At this age, a child no longer needs the more supportive and heavier buggy, because they have the strength and body development to hold themselves upright indefinitely when sitting. They will also spend less time being pushed along by adults, and more time walking alongside them.

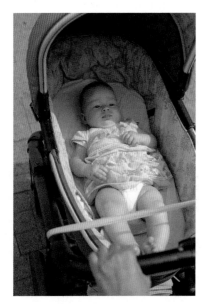

**Figure 2.8** Prams and buggies must be age appropriate

### Reins

Once a baby learns to walk and can do so outside, they are generally keen to explore and to walk independently. They very quickly begin to pick up speed, and it is exciting for a child to be able to head off instantly towards anything that attracts their attention. However, they are still finding their feet and their movements are unpredictable – they can shoot off in any direction and will not know what they should or should not do.

This can make it challenging to keep a toddler safe when you are out walking in the world together, especially when you are using the pavement. Reins can be a very good solution.

- Reins fit around the child's chest and the ends are held by a parent or carer.
- Reins still give a child a feeling of independence as they walk out in front, and as long as they are safe, you can simply follow their lead. But it is very easy to 'put the brakes on' by standing still when they are heading somewhere inappropriate.
- When the child is on reins, you can often save them if they begin to fall, by taking their weight.
- Backpack style reins are also available. The child wears a backpack in the normal way, and detachable reins can be clipped onto the bottom of the bag section.

At around the time a child begins to have more reliable control over their walking, they are usually calmer about being out in the world, and happy to hold an adult's hand on a walk. At this stage, the reins will no longer be needed.

**Figure 2.9** Reins help to keep a toddler safe on a walk

### Car seats

It is not only sensible to use a car seat to keep children safe in the car – it is the law. RoSPA (the Royal Society for the Prevention of Accidents) tells us that this law requires that:

*All children travelling in the front or rear seat of any car, van or goods vehicle must use the correct child car seat until they are either 135 cm in height or 12 years old (whichever they reach first). After this they must use an adult seat belt. There are very few exceptions.*

(www.rospa.com/road-safety/advice/vehicles/car-seats)

Child car seats are only effective when fitted properly in the car, so it is crucial to follow the manufacturer's instructions precisely. Any car seat that has been in a car during an accident must be replaced, even if there is no visible damage. This is because it could have been weakened and might no longer provide the necessary protection.

Only EU-approved child car seats can be used in the UK. These have a label showing a capital 'E' in a circle.

You can choose a car seat based on a child's height or weight.

- Height-based car seats – these are known as 'i-Size' seats. They must be rear-facing until the child is over 15 months old. The child can use a forward-facing car seat when they are over 15 months old. You must check the seat to make sure it is suitable for the height of the child.
- Weight-based car seats – here, the seat the child can use (and the way they must be restrained in it) depends on their weight. You may be able to choose from more than one type of seat.

Childcare professionals are advised to keep an eye on babies during journeys, and avoid making journeys of more than 30 minutes with a young baby. If a longer journey is necessary, taking regular breaks is advised.

Childcare professionals are also advised to limit the use of car seats to the car, so you should not remove the car seat for use as a baby carrier. You should not leave babies to sleep, or put them down to sleep, in a car seat.

**Figure 2.10** Height-based car seat

**Figure 2.11** Weight-based car seat

**Table 2.1** Different types of car seats

| Child's weight | Car seat |
|---|---|
| 0 kg to 9 kg | Lie-flat or 'lateral' baby carrier, *rear-facing baby carrier, or *rear-facing baby seat using a harness |
| 0 kg to 13 kg | *Rear-facing baby carrier or *rear-facing baby seat using a harness |
| 9 kg to 18 kg | *Rear- or forward-facing baby seat using a harness or safety shield |
| 15 kg to 36 kg | *Rear- or forward-facing child seat (highbacked booster seat or booster cushion) using a seat belt, harness or safety shield |

* **You** must also:
• **deactivate** any front airbags before fitting a rear-facing baby seat in a front seat
• **not** fit a child car seat in side-facing seats.

## Baby carrier

There are two types of carrier – those that resemble car seats and those that are baby slings which are worn.

There will usually be both a weight and age limitation given, and it is important not to exceed these criteria.

Take care to ensure that slings are fitted (worn) properly, to ensure that the baby doesn't slip or feel uncomfortable and can breathe unobstructed.

Most carriers are designed to be used when babies are quite young, typically from birth to four months.

### Sleeping equipment

Sufficient sleep is vital to a child's well-being, growth and development. From one to five, the amount of daytime sleep needed will slowly decline, with children eventually going through the day without a nap around the age of three. However, new experiences (such as starting pre-school) and busy days (such as a day trip) will still wear children out, and they may well drop off to sleep – on the ride home in the car for instance.

### Moses basket and cot

Moses baskets are a suitable option for a newborn baby's first bed and up to around three to four months of age, depending on the basket selected and the baby's rate of growth. The manufacturer's guidelines on this will come with the basket.

Moses baskets are designed to be portable. In the early months when a baby is sleeping for much of the time, it is convenient to be able to carry a baby from room to room.

Cots should be sturdy and kept clean. Always ensure that wood is in good condition to avoid splintering. Cots take a lot of wear and tear, especially in a group setting.

The side of the cot that slides down for the lifting in and out of the baby can be particularly prone to wear, so check that it is in good working order. If you notice the sliding mechanism starting to feel slack, report it to the appropriate person straight away, as movement from the baby may cause it to slide down unintentionally. This presents a risk in terms of a baby's body being pinched or trapped, or they may roll and fall from the cot.

Never use a pillow, cot bumper or place toys in the cot (or a Moses basket).

**Figure 2.12** Cots should be sturdy and be kept clean

## Mattresses

Moses baskets come with their own fitted mattresses, uniquely shaped and sized to fit into individual designs, because there is not a standard Moses basket size. However, cot mattresses are generally purchased separately from the cot itself, presenting the buyer with more choice.

## Cot bed/bed

Some children sleep in a special kind of cot known as a 'cot bed'. This means that the cot has been specially designed to turn into the child's first bed with some adjustments when required. Generally, this involves the base of the cot being lowered and the removal of the sides. This can be comforting to the child, because although sleeping in a bed is a new experience, the bed still has a familiar feel.

Other children will go straight from their cot into a child's bed.

Either approach is acceptable. The main focus should be on the bed being sturdy, clean and safe.

## Bed guard

After the safe boundaries of a cot with high sides, there is a risk that a child may fall out of their bed. Bed guards are designed to prevent this when children make the **transition**.

- Bed guards fit onto the bottom of the mattress and are generally made from a steel frame covered with fabric mesh, so the child can see through the guard.
- Many guards are double-sided, but single-sided ones are available (for beds next to a wall). It is also possible to find wooden versions.

While bed guards are widely available and are used by many families, you must be cautious: see the RoSPA guidelines in the Activity.

## Sleeping bag and duvet

A feeling of comfort helps a child to settle down into bed and to get ready for sleep, therefore bedding should be soft to the touch.

Just as for babies, it is important that young children do not get too hot or too cold at night. However, once a child is big enough for a bed, they will also be big enough to throw the covers off should they feel too warm. This means that a child's single duvet or child's single sleeping bag can now be introduced safely.

**Activity**

Find these online RoSPA guidelines:

www.rospa.com/
rospaweb/docs/advice-
services/home-safety/
rospa-home-safety-
position-statements.pdf

**Key term**

**Transition** A process or a period of change from one state or condition to another, when young children usually need support, e.g. starting to eat solid foods, starting pre-school.

**Good practice**

Any sort of transition can be challenging for young children. Getting used to a new cot or bed in a childcare setting certainly falls into this category. Patience, support and understanding are needed. Special stories often help, as they encourage a positive connection between comfort and being in bed.

> ### Case study
>
> Sidra is a childminder. She needs some new bedding for the young children she cares for. She knows that children love to choose their own bedding, and there are many vibrant options, such as superheroes and space rockets. But she wonders if it may be better not to make a bedroom too stimulating overall. Soothing colours and designs are more likely to encourage rest, relaxation and sleep.
>
> - What do you think Sidra should do?

### Rest mats and bean bags

Rest mats may be used for babies and children instead of beds and mattresses in childcare settings. Bean bags may be used for older children. This is because they can be easily stored and brought out when needed. They must carry the appropriate safety mark and be kept clean. When using rest mats for babies, pillows, bumpers and toys should still be avoided. Remember that in mixed age settings, babies should not be left on soft furnishings such as beanbags, or sleep on them with adults.

There has been much research into how sleeping position and bedding (including mattresses) may be a factor in cases of SIDS. For the complete list of advice given to parents for the prevention of SIDS, see Unit R057, section 3.2.

### Feeding equipment

It is important for practitioners to support the chosen feeding methods of parents and carers – breastfeeding, bottle feeding or combination feeding. Quite a lot of equipment is required to support both methods, because it is so important that all feeding equipment is sterilised to ensure that it is hygienic.

### Steriliser and sterilising

Feeding equipment must be washed thoroughly before being sterilised. It should be rinsed, washed and rinsed again. Use bottle brushes and teat brushes for cleaning. Equipment to be washed and sterilised includes:

- bottles
- teats
- bottle caps
- measuring spoons
- breast pump
- plastic knives (used for levelling a spoonful of milk powder when making up feeds).

There are different methods of sterilisation:

1  Traditionally, a sterile solution was made up in a steriliser (a small bucket with a lid) by mixing either sterilising tablets or sterilising liquid with water, following the manufacturer's instructions. The equipment was then submerged in the steriliser for a specified amount of time.

2  Now there is the additional choice of an electric steriliser or a steam steriliser.

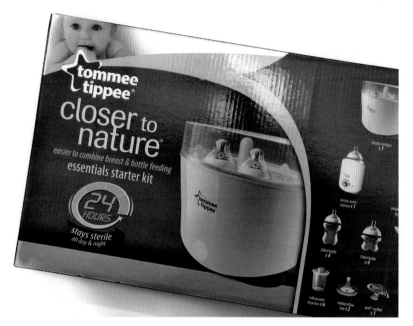

**Figure 2.13** Sterilising equipment

## Bottles

Although only one bottle will be given to a baby at any one time, several bottles are needed in order to always be prepared for feeding.

- Best practice is to make up fresh feeds as they are required, but parents or carers will sometimes need to make up bottles ahead of time and refrigerate them – see section 3.3 for full details.

- It is also best to allow for a few bottles to be in the steriliser at any one time.

There are various teats available, and these should be selected according to the baby's needs.

- The younger the baby, the more slowly they will need to receive their milk. 'Slow' teats have a smaller hole in them to restrict the flow.

- Sometimes, a doctor or health visitor will recommend a teat of a particular shape for a baby who experiences difficulty feeding.

**Figure 2.14** Feeding bottles

## Breast pump

Breast pumps allow mothers to express milk that can then be fed to a baby via a bottle.

- This enables the baby to be fed breast milk even when the mother is away from the baby – for example, a practitioner can give the feed when the mother is at work.

- It also allows other family members to feed the breastfed baby. This can be important to the well-being of some mothers as well as fathers. For example, it means that the task of waking throughout the night to feed a baby can be shared, allowing the mother to get some rest and sleep.

There are two types of breast pump:

- manual
- electric.

From age one, children will become fully weaned onto solid food, and will be growing in confidence as they learn to feed themselves independently.

## Trainer cup

At around 15 months of age, children will be ready for a trainer cup.

- These have a handle at either side, making it easier for a child to hold the cup level and to take it to and from their mouth.

- Trainer cups also have a secure lid to prevent spillages, and a spout to drink from. The spout delivers a much faster flow of liquid than a bottle teat, which children can now cope with.

- When a child has mastered the training cup, the lid can be removed, and they can experience drinking straight from the rim of the cup. Spillages are to be expected, but the use of the two handles will help.

Once a child can lift the training cup to and from their mouth fairly reliably without the lid, they will be ready to switch to a plastic cup with one handle.

**Figure 2.15** Trainer cup

## Cutlery

Babies will start trying to feed themselves by 'helping' their parent or carer with the plastic feeding spoon from the time they are able to sit up in a highchair. They will begin to feed themselves with finger foods (such as cut pieces of fruit) from around 10–12 months and will eventually manage the spoon alone from about 13–15 months.

Once they've mastered this and they are also ready to sit up at the table, it is time to introduce a plastic fork alongside the spoon. A child will generally get used to a fork reasonably quickly, using it to spear soft foods and alternating between the spoon and fork by 15–18 months. They can generally use the two together with precision from around three years.

**Figure 2.16** Cutlery

The next stage is to introduce a knife, and it may also be time to switch over to a nursery set of small metal cutlery with plastic handles. Now things get more complicated. Using a knife and fork requires a child to make a different movement with each hand at the same time, plus hand–eye co-ordination. Learning to use cutlery like an adult is essentially learning to use very tricky tools. Most children have mastered it by the time they are four years old.

## Sectioned plates

Sectioned plates assist with the dishing-up of food for children, as it is easy to monitor how much of each food group they are being served. It also enables easy monitoring of what they do and don't eat.

There are benefits for children too, as the section edges help to keep the food on the plate and makes it easier to 'catch' with cutlery.

## Weaning bibs

**Weaning** is a messy affair! Young children will frequently miss their mouths with a spoonful or forkful of food as they learn to master the complicated hand–eye co-ordination and fine motor skills required to get it there safely.

You should always be relaxed, otherwise children may become tense about eating and begin to dread mealtimes. In the interests of children's well-being and health, it is very important to avoid mealtimes becoming a battleground or standoff.

One of the best ways to achieve this is to make sure that a mess doesn't matter by protecting the child's clothes with a weaning bib. These plastic bibs curl at the end to catch any spilt food or drink, can be removed after the meal and can be washed with the dishes.

## Changing equipment

For at least the first two years, babies and most young children will wear nappies, and in a group setting there will be many nappy changes a day. Most settings require babies and children to arrive with a changing bag from home containing nappies for the day and changes of clothes in case of any mishaps.

The childcare setting will provide a sturdy, durable changing table, topped by a waterproof changing mat. It is essential for staff to clean this with an antibacterial product after every nappy change to ensure good hygiene.

Changing tables often feature shelves beneath the changing surface. These are handy as practitioners need easy access to wet wipes (or an alternative) to clean the child, and to gloves and aprons to wear when doing so.

**Key term**

**Weaning** The process of introducing babies to solid foods.

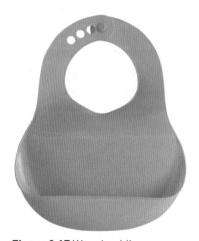

**Figure 2.17** Weaning bib

A safe and hygienic way to dispose of used disposable nappies and other disposable equipment is also required. In the case of non-disposable nappies (such as terry towelling nappies), a safe way to store them and return them to parents for laundering is needed. Nappy sacks are often used.

When practitioners take children off-site, they will take along changing bags containing everything they need to change nappies. Changing bags are designed to open out to reveal a plastic, cleanable lining, which serves as a changing mat when on the go. This can be laid out for use on any safe, flat surface.

## Indoor and outdoor playing for babies and children from birth to five years

It's essential that settings provide a wide variety of appropriate equipment for young children to promote all aspects of development. This also ensures that children can make their own play choices. Play equipment must be age and weight appropriate, safe, of good design, durable and cost effective – you'll learn more about these factors below. Equipment is likely to include:

- Gym sets: such as balls, hoops, quoits, beanbags. These resources wear out over time, so it's important to visually check them each time they are set out and put away. Beanbags can split for instance, spilling the contents.
- Play tents: pop-up tents are particularly popular as instant dens for young children. But the springy way in which they open is somewhat unpredictable, so it is best to pop them up out of the reach of children.
- Painting and craft activities: these are staples of childcare environments. Always be careful to ensure that craft resources are appropriate for the children's age and that there is close supervision when needed – for instance, craft beads can be a choking hazard. Keep an eye on young children who tend to take things to their mouths for exploration – including paint and glue brushes.
- Slides and climbing frames: slides, climbing frames and other large equipment must be sturdy and durable, because this type of apparatus gets much more use in childcare settings than it would in the average family garden at home. The ground beneath them should be safe, e.g. safety flooring or mats may be used.
- Sand boxes: sand boxes (and sandpits) should be filled with specially purchased play sand, safe for children. It's important to choose a sand box with a well-fitting lid for hygiene reasons, especially if used outside, as cats are attracted to sand and may use them as a litter tray.

Also see the section on 'How play benefits development' in Unit R059, Topic area 3, in particular Table 3.4.

**Test your knowledge**

1 Explain why child-sized equipment is important in terms of design.

## Factors affecting suitability and choice for babies and children from birth to five years

### Age and weight appropriateness

As you have learnt, babies develop very quickly in their first year, and this has a continual impact on the equipment that is suitable for them. So you must always check the safety mark and instructions on a piece of equipment (see below) and notice when an item will become unsuitable for a baby in the future. For example:

● It is safe to put a very young baby down to sleep in most Moses baskets. But as the baby grows and becomes able to roll over, they may tip a Moses basket, making it no longer safe.

### Safety

Before using any piece of equipment, it is absolutely vital to check that the item is safe for the child or the children who will use it. This applies to both new pieces of equipment that you are selecting (and perhaps buying) for the first time, and any pieces of equipment that you use regularly.

### Safety labelling

Before buying an item for a child, practitioners need to check that it has a recognised safety mark. These are quality assurance standards that tell you that the item is safe for use as directed by the manufacturer.

It is important that you always use equipment in line with the manufacturer's instructions. This includes making sure items are assembled according to directions. An incorrectly assembled item can be very dangerous. For example:

● A highchair could collapse, causing a child to fall.
● Body parts could be trapped between gaps in a cot.

You must also follow guidelines that appear on boxes and other packaging. For example, it is very common to come across the guideline 'Not suitable for use by children under 36 months due to small parts'.

See Unit R057, section 4.3 for more information.

### Safety features and star ratings

Similar items made by different manufacturers can vary greatly in terms of the safety features offered, so always look at a range of equipment before making a selection.

Product reviews in reputable magazines and online sites are also extremely helpful to consider before purchase. Many will rate different brands, awarding them a number of stars or points.

## Safety checks

All equipment is prone to wear and tear over time, even if durable items have been selected (see the 'durability' section below). This is especially true in group settings and other professional childcare settings (such as a crèche), because over the same period of time, equipment will get much more use than it would in the average family home.

- A previously safe piece of equipment can turn into a hazard when damaged.
- A previously safe baby carrier can become dangerous if the handle stops locking into position.
- A broken rattle may have a sharp edge.
- Damaged footwear may cause a child to slip and fall.
- Damaged wood may cause a splinter.

The best way to ensure that equipment remains safe over time is to visually check it over each time it is set out and put away. This works very well for items such as toys.

Pieces of equipment that tend to stay out can be checked the first time you use them each day – this applies to items such as car seats, cots and baby swings.

- Car seats must be replaced if they have been in a car at the time of an accident – even if damage cannot be seen, they may no longer be safe to use.
- Second-hand car seats should not be bought, as although they may feature a safety mark, you cannot be sure that they have not been in an accident or become otherwise unsafe. You should also consider whether the item is hygienic.
- Some items such as feeding equipment and toys (such as teething rings) will need sterilising.

## Flammability

Flammability is the term used to describe the ability of a substance to ignite or to burn. The more flammable a material is, the greater the fire risk it presents.

To promote safety, there are strict regulations around the materials that manufacturers can use in clothing and other key items for babies, including bedding and soft furnishings.

Flammability is carefully considered when a product is safety tested for a BSI safety mark/kite mark (see Unit R057, section 4.3) – this provides another reason for always checking the safety marks before selecting equipment.

## Stability

Stability is another key safety issue. A high percentage of injuries reported in the UK every year come from falls. It is very important to make sure that any item of equipment that takes a baby's weight or supports a baby's body is stable and secure. Items need to be both well-made and sturdy.

Equipment also needs to be carefully used to ensure stability. For example:

- If heavy shopping bags are placed on the handles of a buggy, it will become unstable and is likely to tip over backwards, putting the baby at risk.
- A baby sling not worn according to the manufacturer's instructions could also be unsafe, as the baby's body may become sore and they may even slip.
- Some pieces of equipment need to be placed on a sturdy, flat surface before use, or stability will be affected. This applies to highchairs, cots and baby swings.

There are also many injuries as a result of objects falling onto a child. Parents and carers need to think carefully about how to prevent objects falling onto babies. This is a particular area of concern at this age, as babies will pull themselves to a standing position and move around the room by holding onto furniture or other nearby equipment.

As well as holding onto items intended for them (such as a baby seat), babies will use anything in reach (such as an adult's chair). So it is best practice to make sure that all such items are sturdy. Larger items that could fall onto a baby if they bumped into them (such as shelving units, TVs and wardrobes) should be fixed to the wall.

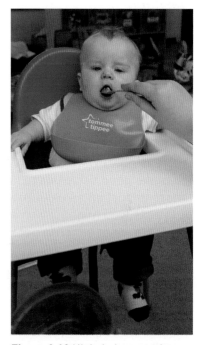

**Figure 2.18** Highchairs must be placed on a sturdy, flat surface

## Hygiene

When completing your safety checks on pieces of equipment (see 'Safety checks' above), you should consider whether the item is hygienic.

- If it is visibly dirty or otherwise unhygienic, you should remove the item for cleaning.
- In the case of large pieces of equipment such as cots, you should remove babies from the vicinity or area and then clean the item.

## Easy to clean

Selecting equipment that is easy to clean helps enormously in terms of keeping things hygienic. Practitioners will have a planned schedule for washing or sterilising appropriate materials and equipment, even if they do not appear to be dirty to the eye. (They will also be washed in between times if necessary as described above.)

Some items such as nappy changing equipment (e.g. a changing mat), feeding equipment and baby toys will need cleaning each time they are used.

Whenever you are cleaning and washing equipment, always make sure that you only use cleaning products that are safe for use with very young children. All cleaning products must be kept out of reach of children.

*Washable*

Items made from fabrics such as bedding will need to be washed frequently, and in some cases after every use. It is sensible to buy fabric items that can be washed easily, ideally in a washing machine. It is also helpful if they can be tumble dried.

## Good practice

As a child gets older, it is good practice to make them increasingly aware of safety issues. This helps them to learn how to make good decisions to keep themselves safe, and becomes more important as children's independence increases. For example, you might say on a trip to the park, 'Please do not climb up there. That bench is not very sturdy and you might fall.'

In addition, young children can increasingly help with hygiene matters, such as wiping the table after a meal or washing the play food in the kitchen sink.

## Activities

1 Working with a partner, reread pages 82–96, focusing on the information given about the age and weight appropriateness of equipment selected for children.
2 Now fill in the table below by making a note of the age and weight information you gathered about each type of equipment.

| Equipment | Information relating to age | Information relating to weight |
|---|---|---|
| Prams and buggies | | |
| Car seats | | |
| Baby carriers | | |
| Moses basket | | |
| Travelling equipment | | |
| Feeding equipment | | |

## Stretch activity

1 Write a short paragraph summarising your learning about the need for equipment that is age and weight appropriate.
2 Begin the paragraph with the sentence below.

'It's very important for practitioners to ensure the equipment selected for a child is appropriate in terms of their age and weight because...'

## Design

Good design influences:

- comfort – how physically comfortable it is to use a product
- accessibility – who can use the product
- ease of use
- aesthetics – how attractive the product is to look at
- adjustability – how flexible the product is.

If you look out for it, you will spot evidence of good design being applied to many pieces of equipment. For example:

- Some feeding bottles have a distinct shape that makes them more comfortable to hold.
- Car seats are moulded to keep a baby comfortable in a position, as well as keeping them safe.

Some cots are lower to the ground than others, making it easier for a shorter person to lift a baby in and out safely.

- A cot may turn into a bed, or a pram may turn into a buggy.
- Bean bags are available in a huge selection of colours and prints.

Design is particularly important when choosing a pram or buggy. If the handles are not at the right height for the person pushing it, their shoulders, back and neck may become sore with prolonged or frequent use.

It is important to think about design for both babies and adults when selecting pieces of equipment.

## Durability

It is always best to select items that are durable (they are made to last). Durable items are made out of tough, strong, hard wearing materials such as wood. There is less chance of durable items being broken and becoming potentially dangerous during use. They are most likely to stand up to regular use by a group of babies or children in a childcare setting.

## Cost

The cost of equipment for a childcare setting can vary depending on the brand. Some brands can be more expensive at the time of purchase, but this is usually because they are made of higher quality materials and last longer. Equipment sold by cheaper brands, which are likely to be made out of cheaper materials, may break or become worn out more quickly and therefore will need to be replaced. For example, a highchair made out of plastic might break more easily than a highchair made out of wood.

> **Good practice**
>
> If you are feeding a child in a carpeted area, protect the floor by placing a wipe-clean mat underneath the child's chair.

> **Test your knowledge** ✔
>
> 1 What is a safety mark?
> 2 When should you replace a car seat?
> 3 What does the term 'durability' mean?

However, there are expensive designer pieces of equipment that are not necessarily more durable than mid-price alternatives. It is fine for a setting to buy these items if they are within their agreed price range, of course, but it often makes sense to buy mid-price alternatives which are just as durable.

## Stretch activity

Search the internet to find two websites selling:

- children's beds
- bed guards
- children's sleeping bags/duvets.
1 Compare the available products for a child transitioning from a cot to their first bed, considering these factors:
   - age appropriateness
   - safety
   - design
   - durability
   - cost.
2 Decide which items you would buy. Write down the details of each item (or copy and paste the information into a Word document and print it out).
3 Give reasons for each of your choices.

## Topic area 3 Nutritional needs of children from birth to five years

### Getting started

What do you already know about dietary requirements for children? With a partner, thought storm advice you are aware of.

How confident are you that this information is accurate and up to date?

## Synoptic link

This area has links to the developmental needs of children from birth to five years, covered in Unit R057, specifically section 3.3.

## 3.1 Current Government dietary recommendations for healthy eating for children from birth to five years

### The reason for Government dietary recommendations

Good nutrition is at the heart of maintaining a healthy body. This is crucial for children's well-being, growth and development. It's so important that the Government issues dietary recommendations to help parents and carers meet the needs of babies and children.

You will learn about the following current Government dietary recommendations below:

- Eatwell Guide
- 5 a day
- British Nutrition Foundation recommendations
- updated recommendations as published in the future.

It's important that you learn what the recommendations are and how to apply them, to ensure that children have a healthy diet.

Children who do not receive good nutrition are at a huge disadvantage. Good nutrition helps to prevent:

- Obesity: it is unhealthy for children to be overweight. Good nutrition, including selecting healthy choices and appropriate portion sizes, is paramount.
- Tooth decay: the British Nutrition Foundation tells us that eating too much sugar and acidic foods is linked to tooth decay, so it is best to keep these foods to mealtimes. Then other foods eaten at the meal will lessen the impact on teeth of any acid produced by fermentation of the sugar.

  It's best to give pre-school children and toddlers water or milk to drink from a cup or free-flowing beaker, rather than from a bottle, as drinking from a bottle is more likely to coat the teeth.

  Drinks containing sugar should be diluted and kept to mealtimes (see 'Drinks' below).
- Failure to thrive: children are diagnosed as failing to thrive when their weight or rate of weight gain is significantly below that expected of a child of their age and gender. Poor nutrition may be an underlying factor.

It's very important that you understand how to meet children's requirements in order to give them the best possible start. Children's nutritional needs change a great deal in their early years.

You will learn about good nutrition for infants from birth to 12 months later in this chapter.

## Eatwell Guide

To help people to get the balance of foods right, the Government have designed the Eatwell Guide (see Figure 2.19). The Eatwell Guide is a pictorial representation of the proportion that different food groups should form in the diet. This representation of food intake relates to people over the age of five, but it is still a very handy visual representation to draw on.

The British Nutrition Foundation tells us that the Eatwell Guide healthy eating guidelines are not intended to apply in full to pre-school children. A diet which is low in fat and high in fibre may be too bulky and not supply enough energy for a young child.

It is recommended, however, that pre-school children (those between the ages of two and five) start to adopt some of the principles of the Eatwell Guide. A healthy family approach to diet and lifestyle should be encouraged, as food preferences are often established during this early stage of life.

## Activity

Visit this website and explore the information about the Eatwell Guide:

**www.nhs.uk/live-well/eat-well/the-eatwell-guide/**

Discuss your learning with a partner.

- Did anything surprise you?
- Support your findings with reasons.

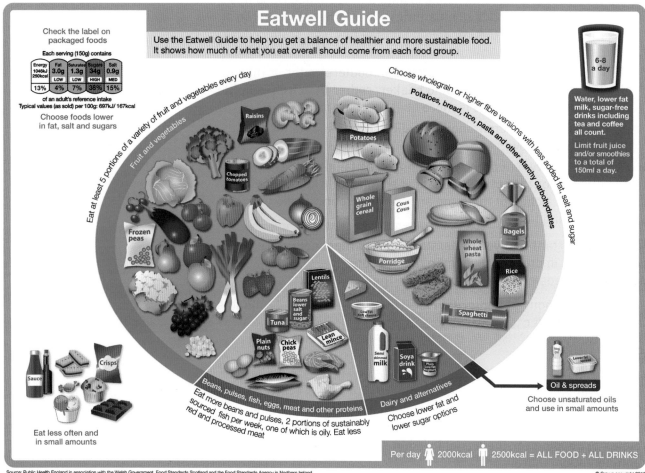

**Figure 2.19** The Eatwell Guide

## 5 a day / fruit and vegetables

Pre-school children and toddlers should be encouraged to eat a variety of different fruit and vegetables, aiming for five portions a day. See Figure 2.20 for the British Nutrition Foundation guidelines.

> There are no specific official guidelines for portion sizes of fruit and vegetables for young children, but portions will be smaller than for adults. Some examples of suggested portion size ranges are ¼–½ an apple, ½–1 tangerine, ½–2 tablespoons of vegetables (e.g. peas, sweetcorn) and 1–4 cherry tomatoes.

**Source:** British Nutrition Foundation

**Figure 2.20** 5 a day for young children

## British Nutrition Foundation recommendations for a healthy diet

### Balanced diet and portion control

It's important for young children to receive a balanced diet containing a variety of food that meets all of their nutritional requirements. (See section 3.4 for essential nutrients and their function.)

Portion control is important.

- If portion sizes are too small, children will not receive the required amount of nutrients, even if all the right foods are offered.
- If portion sizes are too big, children may become obese and develop a habit of eating too much.
- If they are eating too much of one food group, they may eat too little of another food group.

### Consider limiting processed foods/fast foods/snacks/ sugar/fat

Young children need plenty of high energy, nutrient-dense foods. But the following foods should not be given too often, as they are high in fat and sugars (and often salt): chips, ready meals, fast food, pastries, crisps, cakes, biscuits, chocolate and fried foods.

Healthy meals and snacks are the better option.

### Good practice

Avoid using food as a reward, especially sweets or sweet items such as biscuits. It is best not to encourage children to prize sweet foods over healthy foods.

## Encourage healthy foods/snacks

Providing a balanced diet means encouraging children to eat healthy foods and snacks to promote:

- healthy growth
- their development.

The British Nutrition Foundation guidance sets out how this can be achieved. Simply put, children need foods that are high in nutrients and which provide sufficient:

- protein
- vitamins
- minerals.

There are four main food groups. Adults should select from these to create a daily diet consisting of small meals, snacks and drinks.

## Group 1: Starchy foods

Starchy foods include bread, pasta, rice, breakfast cereals, potatoes, couscous, chapatis and yams. Read Table 2.2 to find out more about them.

**Table 2.2** Food group 1

| Amount children should consume daily aged 1–5 years | Portion size | What starchy foods provide | Notes |
|---|---|---|---|
| 5 servings – at least one with each meal, plus snacks. A variety should be offered. | This will depend on the age of a child and their current appetite, for example a portion of cereal may be quarter of a child-sized bowl for one child, and half a bowl for another child. | • Essential nutrients.<br>• Energy, which is important for growth and to fuel a child's daily activities. | Because wholemeal starchy foods are more filling than non-wholemeal equivalents, they should only be offered occasionally. This makes it easier for children to eat the amount of food they need for energy. |

**Figure 2.21** Children should have five portions of starchy foods per day

## Group 2: Milk and dairy foods

As well as milk, this group includes cheese (hard cheeses, cream cheese and cottage cheese), yoghurt and fromage frais.

**Table 2.3** Food group 2

| Amount children should consume daily aged 1–5 years | Portion size | What milk and dairy foods provide | Notes |
|---|---|---|---|
| Minimum of 300 ml (half a pint) of milk, or three portions of other dairy foods. | This will depend on the age of a child and their appetite, but suggestions are:<br>• **1–3 years:**<br>  • 80 g of yoghurt = one portion<br>  • 15 g cheese = one portion<br>• **4–5 years:**<br>  • 100 g of yoghurt = one portion<br>  • 20 g cheese = one portion | • Excellent source of calcium, which is required for good bone development.<br>• Essential nutrients including protein and vitamin B12.<br>Eggs are sometimes mistaken for a dairy food but are actually a non-dairy source of protein. | Children aged 1–5 years should ideally be given whole milk and full-fat dairy items. From 2 years, semi-skimmed milk may be provided for a child growing well and eating a healthy balanced diet. Skimmed milk does not provide the necessary nutrients for children under 5. |

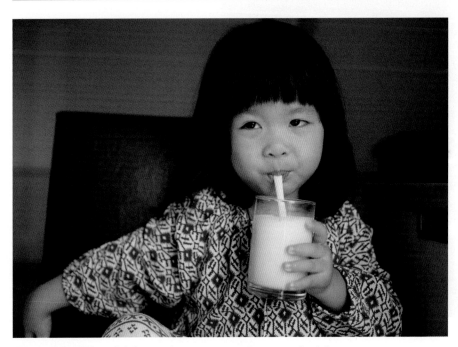

**Figure 2.22** Milk and dairy products are a good source of calcium

## Group 3: Non-dairy sources of protein

This includes meat, fish, eggs, beans, tofu and soya. Quorn can also be a source of protein but should not be given to children under three years.

**Table 2.4** Food group 3

| Amount children should consume daily aged 1–5 years | Portion size | What non-dairy sources of protein provide | Notes |
|---|---|---|---|
| 2–3 portions a day. If a child is vegetarian or vegan, 3 portions should be offered. | This will depend on the age of a child and their appetite, but suggestions are:<br>• **1–3 years:** 14.5 g = one portion<br>• **4–5 years:** 19.7 g = one portion | Essential nutrients including protein and calcium, iron and vitamins B and D. These are important for growth and development. They are also needed to maintain and repair the body. | • For vegetarians and vegans: mixing protein foods together helps provide balanced nutrients. Giving a vitamin-C-rich drink (such as fruit juice) with protein foods helps the body absorb iron.<br>• Quorn must only be given from the age of 3. |

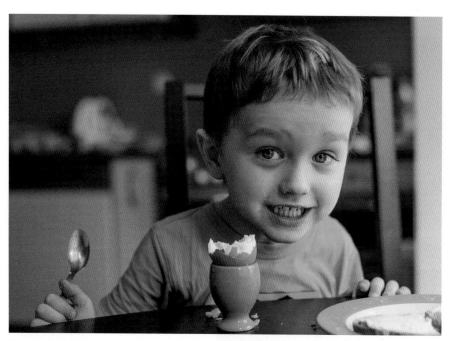

**Figure 2.23** Eggs are a good source of protein

*Group 4: Fruit and vegetables*
See '5 a day' on page 101.

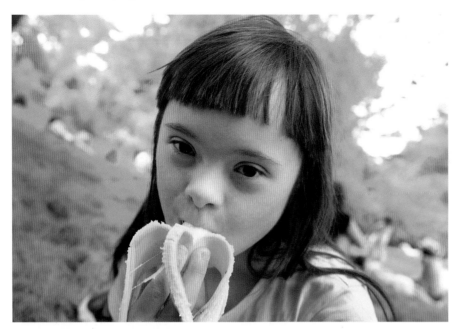

**Figure 2.24** Fruit is a good choice for a healthy snack

**Good practice**

The British Nutrition Foundation recommends giving children aged six months to five years liquid supplement drops that contain vitamins A, C and D. This is especially important for children who do not eat a balanced and varied diet.

## *Consider limiting salt content*

A balanced, healthy diet will not contain too much salt. This is important because excess salt can lead to raised blood pressure. In later life, raised blood pressure can increase the risk of someone developing heart disease or having a stroke. The recommended daily salt intakes are:

- a maximum of 2 g (0.8 g sodium) for children aged one to three years
- a maximum of 3 g (1.2 g sodium) for children aged four to six years.

You can take steps to reduce a child's salt intake. The British Nutrition Foundation tips for doing so are summarised in Figure 2.25.

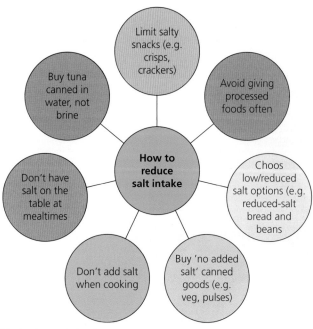

**Figure 2.25** Reducing salt intake

## Consider limiting fizzy drinks/fruit juice

Water and milk are the recommended drinks for children aged one to five years. Sugary drinks can cause tooth decay. Drinks containing sugar include:

- fruit squashes
- fruit juices
- flavoured milks
- iced slush drinks
- fizzy drinks
- flavoured yoghurt drinks.

If a child is to be permitted sweet drinks occasionally, it is best to offer unsweetened fruit juice diluted with water. This should only be given at a mealtime.

## Foods to avoid

The British Nutrition Foundation recommends avoiding some foods for children aged one to five years. Find out more in Table 2.5 below.

**Table 2.5** Foods to avoid

| Food to be avoided | Reason for avoiding | Notes |
|---|---|---|
| Salt | Can lead to raised blood pressure. | See above for recommended levels of salt. |
| Sugar (sweet foods and drinks) | Potential tooth decay. | Limit the amount offered. Only provide at mealtimes. |
| Raw eggs | Risk of salmonella poisoning. | Cook until white and yolk are solid. |
| Low-calorie and low-fat foods | These can prevent children from getting enough nutrients and sufficient energy. | Energy is needed for healthy growth and as fuel for physical activities throughout the day. |
| Nuts | Choking risk. | This applies to both whole nuts and chopped nuts. |

## Stretch activity

Find a partner to work with and look at the current Government recommendations. Label yourselves A and B.

1 A should explain to B what is meant by providing a balanced diet.
2 B should explain the Eatwell Guide to A.
3 Together, look through the recommendations – did either of you miss anything out? If so, make notes about the missing information. This will help you to remember it.
4 Together, now create a leaflet to inform busy parents with young children about the importance of making healthy choices for their children. Include details about the Eatwell Guide.

## Updated recommendations as published in the future

Nutritional advice and recommendations from the Government change over time. It's important that you:

● remain aware of any updated published recommendations
● promote them in your work with babies and children.

### Test your knowledge

1 The Government recommend '5 a day' of which food group?
2 Why should you stop giving milk in a bottle to children over 12 months?
3 Name three different foods you should consider limiting.

### Good practice

Children below the age of five with small appetites, who need energy-dense diets, should not be restricted in their fat intake.

### Activity

Visit the British Nutrition Foundation website and read the key points in the Nutrition for Life – Toddlers and pre-school children section:

**https://www.nutrition.org. uk/life-stages/toddlers- and-pre-school/**

## 3.2 Essential nutrients and their functions for children from birth to five years

### Getting started

Mealtimes, or feeding times for babies, provide opportunities for children and adults to be close and to bond. Children place a lot of trust in the adults who feed them, especially when they are physically being fed. You can explore this for yourself.

● Pair up with someone else.
● Choose a food you like that can easily be eaten from a spoon, such as yoghurt.
● Place your trust in the other person and allow them to feed you a few spoonfuls.
● Swap roles and feed your partner a few spoonfuls.
● Discuss how it felt. Did you trust the other person? Did you feel a little vulnerable? Did they feed you at the right speed? Discuss and justify all your answers.

Nutrients are the nourishment that come from the food you eat. In this section, you will learn about the function of nutrients – what each nutrient does for the body.

You will also learn about sources of nutrients, or the types of food that contain certain nutrients. For example, under the heading 'Protein', you will see that sources of protein include meat and beans.

The body needs nutrients and water to promote growth and development, and to regulate body processes. Read on to find out more about them.

## Nutrients

### Proteins

Protein foods are made up of amino acids. Sources of protein can be divided into two categories:

1 animal sources – including meat, poultry, fish, milk and eggs
2 vegetable sources – including soya, tofu, beans, pulses and textured vegetable protein (TVP).

The functions of all proteins are to aid growth and repair. They make new cells as babies and children grow and develop. They also replace damaged cells and repair tissue when children injure themselves.

### Carbohydrates

Sources of carbohydrates can be divided into two categories:

1 starches – including bread, pasta, potatoes, rice, cereals, beans
2 sugars – including fruit, honey, sweets, beet sugar, cane sugar.

The functions of carbohydrates are to produce energy. They are broken down into glucose within a child's body and are absorbed into their bloodstream. Sugars are easily converted and can provide children with a quick, short-lasting energy boost. Starches take longer to convert and releases energy more slowly, providing children with a longer-lasting supply of energy.

### Fats

Sources of fats can be divided into three categories:

1 saturated fats – including butter, milk, cheese, meat (all animal sources), palm oil (vegetable source)
2 unsaturated fats – including olive oil and nut oil (vegetable sources)
3 polyunsaturated fats – including oily fish (animal sources), corn oil, sunflower oil (vegetable sources).

> **Key term**
> **Nutrients** The nourishment that comes from the food we eat.

> **Good practice**
> The NHS tells us that starchy foods should make up just over one-third of everything we eat. This means we should base our meals on these foods.
>
> They advise trying to choose some wholegrain or wholemeal varieties of starchy foods, such as brown rice, wholewheat pasta and wholemeal or higher fibre white bread. They contain more fibre, and usually more vitamins and minerals than white varieties.

The functions of fats are to produce warmth and protection. The layer of fat under children's skin provides insulation to keep them warm. Thin layers of fat also protect the vital internal organs within the child's body.

## Vitamins A, B group, C, D, E, K

Children need a regular supply of water-soluble vitamins as these cannot be stored in the body. Fat-soluble vitamins can be stored in the body but intake should still be regular.

Table 2.6 sets out the sources and functions of the main vitamins. Many are key in the promotion of health and prevention of disease.

**Good practice**

Regularly consuming foods and drinks high in sugar increases the risk of obesity and tooth decay.

**Table 2.6** Vitamins

| Vitamin | Source | Function | Type | Deficiency |
|---|---|---|---|---|
| A | Cheese, butter, eggs, oily fish, tomatoes, carrots. | Promotes growth and development. Maintenance of good vision and healthy skin. | Fat soluble. | Deficiency may lead to skin conditions and vision impairment. |
| B group | Meat, chicken, eggs, fish, green leafy vegetables, dates, pulses. Some breakfast cereals are fortified with vitamin B (meaning it is added to them). | Promotes healthy functioning of the nerves and muscles. | Water soluble. Very regular intake required. | Deficiency may lead to anaemia and wasting of the muscles. |
| C | Fruit: oranges, strawberries and blackcurrants have a high content. | Maintenance of healthy tissue and skin. Prevention of disease. | Water soluble. Daily intake required. | Deficiency leads to decreased resistance to infection and can result in scurvy. |
| D | Oily fish and fish oil, egg yolk. Milk, margarine and some breakfast cereals are fortified with vitamin D. Sunlight on the skin can cause the body to produce vitamin D. | Maintenance of bones and teeth. Assists body growth. | Fat soluble. | Deficiency in children may lead to bones which do not harden properly (rickets). Also leads to tooth decay. |
| E | Cereals, egg yolk, seeds, nuts, vegetable oils. | Promotes blood clotting and healing. | Fat soluble. | Deficiency may result in delayed blood clotting. |
| K | Whole grains, green vegetables, liver. | Promotes healing. Necessary for blood clotting. | Fat soluble. | Deficiency may lead to excessive bleeding due to delayed blood clotting. Usually given to babies after birth as a deficiency is sometimes seen in newborns, although rare in adults. |

## Minerals

Minerals such as calcium, iron and zinc are needed for a variety of bodily functions. For example:

- building strong bones and teeth
- healthy red blood cells, skin and hair

- nerve function
- muscle function
- metabolic processes such as turning food into energy.

So in turn, minerals are necessary for:

- the body to work properly, including healing wounds
- growth and development
- maintaining normal health and immune system (preventing disease).

**Figure 2.26** Minerals are needed for strong teeth and bones

**Table 2.7** Minerals

| Mineral | Source | Function | Deficiency |
|---|---|---|---|
| Calcium | Milk, cheese, eggs, fish, pulses, wholegrain cereals. White and brown flour are fortified with calcium | Required for strong teeth and bones. Also for nerve and muscle function. | Deficiency may lead to rickets and tooth decay. |
| Iron | Red meat and offal, eggs, green vegetables, dried fruits | Required for the formation of haemoglobin in the red blood cells, which transport oxygen around the body. | Deficiency may lead to anaemia. |
| Zinc | Meat, poultry, seafood, legumes, whole grains, fortified breakfast cereals | Required to make new cells for growth and to heal damaged tissue. Also helps the immune system. | Deficiency may lead to lower immunity and wounds taking longer to heal. |
| Sodium chloride (salt). Too much salt is bad for children. **It must not be added** to food for babies or young children during food preparation or at the table. | Salt, meat, fish, bread, processed food | Required for the formation of haemoglobin in the red blood cells, which transport oxygen around the body. | |

## Fibre

Fibre is an important part of a healthy balanced diet. It adds roughage to food. Its functions are:

- to encourage a child's body to pass out the waste products of food after it has been digested, by stimulating the bowel muscles
- to help prevent constipation, irritable bowel syndrome and cancers of the bowel
- to improve digestive health.

Sources of fibre include:

- fruit, such as bananas, apples
- dried fruit
- wholemeal pasta
- beans and lentils
- peas
- sweetcorn
- carrots
- oats.

**Good practice**

Children aged two to five years need about 15 g of fibre a day. The NHS reports that many people do not have enough fibre in their diet. Sources of fibre include:

- wheat bran
- wholegrain cereals
- corn.

## Water

All the main systems in the body depend on water. Water maintains fluid in the cells of the body and in the bloodstream. It also contains some minerals.

The human body is up to 70 per cent water, and much of it is:

- lost through urine and sweat
- lost in the form of vapour from the lungs during breathing
- used to turn food into energy.

So water needs to be replaced very regularly.

Without any water, all life forms will die. The functions of water include:

- hydration
- regulating body temperature
- carrying nutrients and oxygen to cells.

Dehydration occurs when someone does not get enough water. Symptoms include headaches, tiredness and finding it difficult to concentrate.

Water is required by the body for the following functions:

- to flush waste products from the kidneys
- to lubricate joints
- to moisten the eyes, mouth and nose
- to dissolve minerals and other nutrients, making them accessible for the body
- to protect organs and tissues
- to prevent constipation.

In addition to plain water, sources of water include:

- fruit juice
- milk
- fruit.

**Figure 2.27** Children must stay hydrated

## Food sources to meet nutritional needs

You have learnt that young children grow and develop very quickly in their early years. This means that their nutritional requirements are continually changing, as they depend on children's age, weight and height.

It is important to know how to respond to these needs. Until the age of around six months old, babies will be fed only on milk, and will receive no solid food at all. Milk can provide them with all the nutrients they need at this age.

### Activity

Write a paragraph explaining the functions and sources of protein, vitamins, minerals, fibre and water to parents. This should be suitable for inclusion in a pre-school's newsletter.

## Birth to six months

At this age, children will be fed either:

- breast milk
- formula milk
- a combination of breast milk and formula milk.

Newborn babies only take a small amount of milk to start with, but by the time they are a week old, most will need around 150 to 200 ml of milk per kilo of their weight per day until they are six months old. But be aware that this amount will vary from baby to baby.

By the age of around six months, a baby's digestive system will have developed fully, meaning that they can cope well with solid foods.

You will find further information about feeding babies aged from birth to six months in section 3.3.

## Formula milk

There are different types of formula milks:

- anti-reflux milk – for babies who experience difficulties with reflux, such as bringing up a significant amount of their feed
- lactose-free milk – given when a baby is lactose intolerant (lactose is present in breast milk and formula milk)
- soya milk – a popular solution when a baby is lactose intolerant
- hungry baby milk – for babies who are not satisfied by a regular feed. Use of this is generally best when advised by a GP or health visitor.
- goat's milk – this is produced to the same nutritional standards as cow's milk formula. It cannot be fed to babies who have a cow's milk allergy as the milks contain similar proteins.
- anti-colic milk – colic symptoms can sometimes be caused by lactose sugars, so lactose-free milk may be recommended for some babies by a GP or dietitian. Lactose intolerance can come and go, and might last only a few days or weeks, so the need for anti-colic milk can be very short lived.

**Good practice**

The weight gain of a baby indicates whether the baby is getting enough milk. Babies are generally weighed at birth and between five and ten days. After this, babies aged from birth to six months should be weighed once a month.

The weight is recorded in the Personal Child Health Record, provided for parents by the NHS. If parents are concerned about their baby's weight gain, they can speak to their health visitor, who will offer advice and support.

### Six to twelve months

At around six months, babies are ready to begin the weaning process. This is the process in which babies are introduced to solid foods. There are three stages:

1 Weaning Stage 1: babies are introduced gradually to solids, generally starting with baby rice and moving on to pureed fruit and vegetables.
2 Weaning Stage 2: babies are introduced to minced foods such as chicken, and finger foods such as rusks and toast.
3 Weaning Stage 3: babies are introduced to solid foods such as pasta and cheese.

### Weaning Stage 1

At first, babies should be offered a small amount of bland, warm food of a loose or sloppy consistency. This should not contain salt, gluten or sugar. Baby rice or banana mixed with milk from the baby's bottle are ideal.

Half to a full teaspoon is enough to start with. This can then be gradually increased.

As the baby begins to take more food and moves onto pureed fruit and vegetables, the amount of milk they receive should be decreased.

### Weaning Stage 2

Once they are used to the foods in Stage 1, babies can have:

- soft, cooked meat such as minced chicken
- other foods such as pasta, noodles, toast, lentils, rice and mashed hard-boiled eggs
- full-fat dairy products such as yoghurt, fromage frais or custard with no added sugar or less sugar.

Whole cows' milk can be used in cooking or mixed with food from six months.

Finger food allows a child to learn to chew. It should be cut into pieces big enough for a baby to hold in their fist with part of the food still visible (pieces about the size of your own finger).

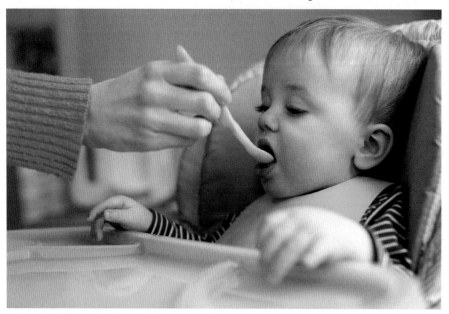

**Figure 2.28** Weaning Stage 2

## *Weaning Stage 3*

By the age of 12 months, a baby will have gradually moved towards eating three meals a day that include solid foods. Their diet should consist of a variety of fruit and vegetables, bread, rice, pasta, potatoes and other starchy foods, meat, fish, eggs, pieces of cheese, beans and other non-dairy sources of protein, as well as milk and dairy products.

At 12 months, a baby can drink

- whole cows' milk
- unsweetened fruit juice diluted with water.

You will find further information about weaning in section 3.3.

### Good practice

Some children have special dietary requirements. These may be due to food allergies, which can be severe and life-threatening (such as a nut allergy). They can also relate to medical conditions, culture, ethnicity or religious or ethical beliefs. Therefore it is very important to check whether a child has special dietary requirements, and if so, you must be sure that you fully understand them.

### Case study

Gen is a nanny. She has just started working with ten-month-old Ted, who is lactose intolerant and drinks soya milk. She has not come across this before.

Gen asks to sit down with Ted's parents to fully talk it over. At the end of the conversation she considers whether she understands how to meet Ted's dietary needs. She wants to make sure that she understands how to use soya milk in recipes, as Ted will soon be ready to eat a wider range of foods. She starts off by searching the NHS website (www.nhs. uk) and the Government's food advice website (www.food.gov.uk).

1 Do you think Gen is looking in the right place for further information? Give reasons for your answer.
2 What else do you think Gen could do to help her meet Ted's dietary needs?

### One to five years

Planning menus is the best way to meet the nutritional requirements of children from one to five years. Menus should

- cater for main meals, snacks and drinks
- promote the nutritional balance that is needed for a healthy diet overall.

It is important to look at the bigger picture, rather than thinking about each meal or snack in isolation. For example, what did a child eat for their last meal? What will they eat next? Other considerations are shown in Figure 2.29.

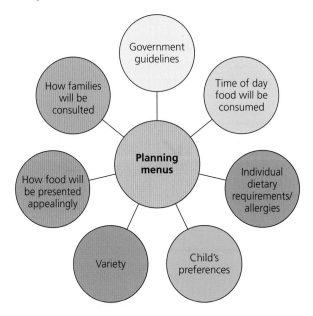

**Figure 2.29** Meeting nutritional requirements. Why do you think families should be consulted about menus?

You will learn more about planning and preparing a feed/meal in section 3.3.

## Main food groups

The meals, snacks and drinks that feature on a menu should be drawn from the main food groups. This includes the following staples:

- bread, other cereals, potatoes, rice, pasta, beans
- fruit and vegetables, such as oranges, apples, peas, carrots
- milk and dairy, such as cheese, yoghurt
- meat, fish and alternatives, such as poultry, eggs, Quorn.

## Fatty and sugary foods

Fatty and sugary foods (e.g. chocolate, crisps, biscuits and sweets) may be offered in small portions as an occasional treat. But they should not feature regularly in a young child's diet. Fatty and sugary foods offer little in the way of good nutrition, and too many fatty and sugary foods are bad for children's health.

Some parents or carers may permit the occasional sugary fizzy drink. However, they are full of sugar and so are particularly harmful to children's teeth. It is better for children aged one to five years not to have fizzy drinks.

---

### Activity

1 Visit this NHS weblink and read more about what to feed young children:

**www.nhs.uk/conditions/baby/weaning-and-feeding/what-to-feed-young-children/**

2 Follow at least four of the weblinks given on the NHS webpage, and read the information you come across. Make notes of any key points that you would like to remember.

---

### Test your knowledge

1 Name the three categories of sources of fats.
2 In addition to plain water, name three other sources of water.
3 At what age does the weaning process take place?
4 Why should fatty and sugary foods only be offered in small portions as an occasional treat?

## 3.3 Plan for preparing a feed/meal

When planning to prepare a feed or meal, there are some important things to consider, as shown in Figure 2.30. Let's look at each of these in turn.

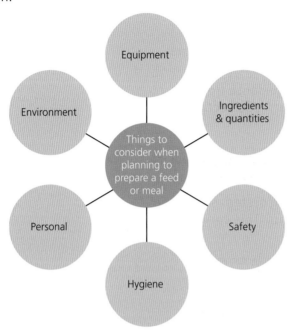

**Figure 2.30** Things to consider when planning to prepare a feed or meal

### Synoptic link

This subject has links to Unit R057, specifically section 4.3.

### Equipment

It's essential to have the right equipment available to prepare feeds or meals. Basic equipment includes:

- steriliser
- bottles
- scales
- knives (including sharp knives)
- spoons
- peeler
- masher
- chopping boards
- pots/pans/bowls.

In advance of preparing feeds or meals, make sure the right equipment is ready to use. This includes making sure:

- equipment is clean, hygienic and in good order
- equipment used to prepare feeds is sterilised.

## Ingredients and quantities

As you've learnt, you need to research and understand the nutritional value of specific foods and meals. This allows you to plan menus that promote healthy eating for children. You also need to know the right quantity to offer to children. To achieve this you can consider:

- labelling (of commercially produced foods)
- software/apps (usually called nutritional analysis programmes, which help with working out nutritional values)
- Eatwell Guide/British Nutrition Foundation guidance (food guidelines recommended by the Government – see section 3.1).

### *Labelling*

Food labelling enables you to see what is in commercially produced (manufactured) food, to help you to make healthy choices.

The Food Standards Agency traffic light labelling system shows the amount of fat, sugar, saturates and salt in grams. This corresponds to a traffic light colour, as shown in Figure 2.31.

**Figure 2.31** Traffic light label

The labelling works as follows:

- Red = a high quantity
- Amber = a medium quantity
- Green = a low quantity.

You will see that the number of calories contained is also included on the label.

### *Calories*

Once children are fully weaned, at around 12 months old, it is time to think about the number of calories they consume. The chart in Figure 2.32 shows the estimated number of calories needed by children each day. You will see that boys require more calories than girls. The calories for adults are also included so you can make a comparison.

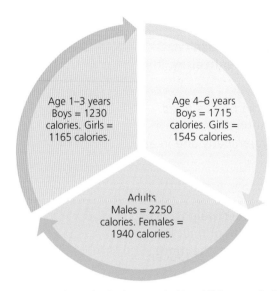

**Figure 2.32** Estimated number of calories needed by children each day

## Software/apps

A range of software and apps are available to help adults with nutritional analysis.

- Some software/apps contain more information than others.
- Some software/apps provide a breakdown of nutritional information for foods that are not manufactured (such as fruits and vegetables), like the type of information you would expect to see on a food label. This is extremely helpful.
- Other software/apps provide menus for children of various ages, based on their age, weight and growth.

## Eatwell Guide/British Nutrition Foundation

You were introduced to the Eatwell Guide and British Nutrition Foundation in section 3.1. Now is a good time to recap that information.

## Portion size for children aged one to five years

What a child eats is not the only thing that matters. The correct portion size is also key (see section 3.1 for more information).

It is very easy to overlook the extra calories contained in drinks such as smoothies, fruit juices and fizzy drinks for older children.

If you are concerned that a child is eating too much or too little:

- Track their food intake for a few days, recording everything they eat and the portion sizes. Foods can be weighed out if necessary.
- Then, using food labels and calorific tables, or using software/apps, work out how many calories children have eaten.
- If the calorie intake is too high or too low, future portion sizes can be adjusted.

> **Activity**
>
> Are you surprised by the recommendations in Figure 2.32? Explain, giving reasons.

> **Activity**
>
> Type 'apps for child nutrition' into a search engine. Investigate the results: look for apps that are suitable both for planning and tracking nutrition.

## Feeds for babies aged from birth to six months

Babies will not get sufficient nutrition if their formula doesn't contain enough powder, but too much powder is also unhealthy. It is important to get the amount exactly correct.

It is very important to follow directions when feeding babies aged from birth to six months so that they get the nutrition they need. If the baby is bottlefed, this must be done safely, hygienically and in an unrushed, caring manner.

## Bottle feeding

The amount of milk given to babies will depend on their weight. Over a 24-hour period, babies generally need around 150 ml of milk for each kilogram of their weight. So the bigger a baby gets, the more milk they will need.

Babies should be fed when they are hungry at first, known as 'feeding on demand'. Babies will then settle into a routine with feeds at regular intervals. Every baby is different, but newborns need around eight feeds a day at approximately four-hour intervals.

To calculate how much milk babies need:

- Divide the amount of food needed each day by the number of feeds.
- Follow current best practice guidelines and the parent or carer's wishes.

You learnt about different types of formula milk in section 3.2. You might like to recap this now.

The current NHS advice is to make up feeds at the time they are required as far as possible, in order to minimise the risk of food poisoning.

If a baby needs to be fed away from home:

- Take a measured-out amount of formula in a small dry container, plus a flask of boiled water and an empty sterilised bottle. This will enable a fresh feed to be made up – the water must still be hot when it is used.
- The bottle should be cooled under running water before the baby is fed.
- Ready-to-use formula could be used instead.

If this is not possible, or you need to take a ready-prepared feed to another location such as a nursery:

- Prepare the feed at home and cool it at the back of the fridge.
- Take it out just before leaving home and transport it in a cool bag with an ice pack.
- Store it in the back of a fridge when you reach your destination.
- It must be used within four hours of its preparation.

## Expressed breast milk

Breast pumps must always be sterilised before use. It is also possible for mothers to express milk by hand, and in this case, the milk should be caught in a sterilised feeding bottle or container.

Once expressed, breast milk can be stored in a sterilised container. It can be stored:

- in the fridge for up to five days at 4°C or lower
- for two weeks in the ice compartment of a fridge
- for up to six months in a freezer.

If milk has been frozen:

- Defrost it in the fridge.
- Once defrosted, use it straight away.
- Do not refreeze milk once it is thawed.

Expressed milk can be taken from the home fridge, transported (e.g. to nursery) in a cool bag with deep-frozen ice-packs, then transferred to the fridge on arrival. Wrapping the ice-packs in kitchen roll first prevents the milk becoming frozen.

Previously refrigerated breast milk can be kept cool (10°C or below) for up to 24 hours when in a well-insulated bag with deep-frozen ice-packs.

Depending on what a baby prefers, expressed milk can be given either straight from the fridge, or warmed to body temperature. To warm milk, place the bottle in lukewarm water (a jug of water works well).

**Figure 2.33** Breast pumps can be used to express breast milk

## Safety

Many tasks carried out in food preparation are potentially dangerous, so it's important to think carefully about safety and take appropriate precautions. In childcare settings, you should always follow policies and procedures which will have been developed after risk assessments have been carried out.

Safety precautions include:

- using knife blocks to store sharp knives safely
- using different coloured chopping boards, one for meat, one for other foods, to avoid cross-contamination of raw food
- mopping up spillages as soon as they occur
- using appliances (such as kettles) with curly flexes, which make it more difficult for an appliance to be pulled over
- using a cooker guard
- using the back hob spots
- turning the handles of pots and pans inward, to prevent burns, scalds and spillages.

The following are guidelines for safe food storage:

- Ensure that food in the fridge and freezer is cold enough – use a thermometer to check. Fridges should be below 5°C. Freezers should be –18°C maximum. They must be cleaned and defrosted regularly.
- Cool food quickly before placing it in the fridge.
- Cover stored food or wrap it with cling film.
- Label items with a correct use-by date if necessary.
- Separate raw and cooked food. Store raw food at the bottom of the fridge, and cooked food higher up, so that raw juices (should they spill) will not contaminate cooked food.
- If food has started to thaw, never refreeze it.
- Ensure food is fully thawed before cooking.

The following are guidelines for safe food preparation for children:

- Cook food thoroughly (e.g. cook eggs until firm, and cook meat all the way through).
- Test chicken to check it is cooked properly.
- Do not reheat food.

**Figure 2.34** Fridges must be kept at the correct temperature

## Hygiene

Effective food hygiene practices are crucial to children's health and well-being because they prevent food poisoning.

You need to know how to ensure that food is stored, prepared and cooked safely, and that food areas are kept hygienically. Hygiene practices fall into these three categories:

- personal hygiene
- environment/equipment hygiene
- sterilisation.

### Personal hygiene

Your own personal hygiene is vital because you will be handling food for consumption. The personal hygiene of the children who will be eating and drinking is just as important. You should:

- Wash your hands with antiseptic soap before and after handling food.
- Use waterproof dressings to cover any cuts or grazes on your hands.

**Good practice**

Practitioners handling or preparing food in a group setting should attend a course on food hygiene to gain a Basic Food Hygiene certificate.

- Never cough or sneeze over food.
- Tie back long hair.
- Wear protective clothing (such as an apron) that is only used for food preparation.

Teach children the following:

- They must wash hands thoroughly with antibacterial soap before eating and drinking.
- In group settings, children's hands must be dried with paper towels or a hand drier.
- Open wounds on hands must be covered with a plaster.
- They must only touch the food they are going to eat, so they should not pick up food and then put it back. It is fine to leave food they do not want to finish on their plate.
- Food and drink should not be taken from other people's plates or cups. They should not share cutlery or eat food someone else has bitten.
- They must not eat food that has fallen on the floor, or eat from cutlery or plates that have been on the floor.
- They should avoid blowing their nose, coughing or sneezing near food.

### Environment

Kitchen and eating areas should be kept clean at all times.

- Surfaces such as tables and worktops should be wiped down using an antibacterial spray before and after food preparation/serving meals.
- All equipment used, from kitchen appliances to cutlery, must also be kept hygienically. It should be washed thoroughly after use, in hot water.

### Sterilisation – sterilising bottles and feeding equipment

It is necessary to sterilise all feeding equipment for babies up to the age of 12 months. This includes the equipment needed to feed expressed milk to babies. You will need to:

- choose the sterilising method (e.g. steam or water)
- wash the equipment to prepare it for the steriliser
- follow manufacturer's instructions for your selected sterilising method (see the case study example below).

**Test your knowledge**

1 What information does a traffic light food label give?
2 Which pieces of feeding equipment used in the preparation and feeding of babies aged from birth to 12 months should be sterilised before use?

## Case study

Jurgen is a child minder. After feeding 10-month-old Nell, he washes his hands and washes the feeding equipment he used. He rinses it, washes it and rinses it again.

He makes up some sterilising solution by following the manufacturer's instructions. He measures out the right amount of water in a jug and pours it into the steriliser unit (a pail with a lid). He adds the right number of sterilising tablets and they dissolve. He submerges the equipment in the water and leaves them for the amount of time as the instructions state.

When the time has passed, he washes his hands again and places the items on the drainer to dry. He then stores them in a container with a lid.

1   Why did Jurgen wash his hands twice?
2   Why do you think the sterilised items are kept in a container with a lid?

## 3.4 How to evaluate planning and preparation of a feed/meal

### Getting started

What factors do you think would be important to a child when they are given food that has been prepared?

It's important to evaluate the planning and preparation of feeds/meals, so that improvements can be made over time. It is helpful to consider:

- verbal or written feedback you receive from practitioners, parents and carers
- feedback from children themselves
- whether a child is enjoying the foods they are given.

### Comparisons

Making comparisons is a very helpful part of the process. You can consider whether current guidelines for a balanced nutritious diet are being met, for example:

- 5 a day
- the Eatwell Guide
- British Nutrition Foundation guidance
- calorie recommendations.

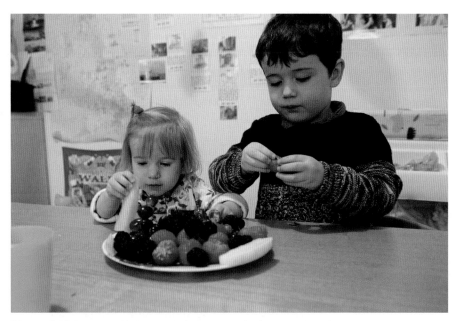

**Figure 2.35** Are the children enjoying the foods they are given?

## Strengths/weaknesses

The next part of the evaluation process is to think carefully about the feedback you have gathered to identify strengths and weaknesses. For example:

- If a child doesn't always eat their five fruit and vegetables each day, this is a weakness.
- If they usually enjoy their meals and eat well, this is a strength.

## Improvements/changes

Now it is time to identify what improvements or changes you should make to address the weaknesses. For example, you might decide to increase the amount of fruit eaten by:

- introducing a breakfast fruit smoothie to a child's diet, or
- giving them a fresh juice drink with their usual piece of fruit at snack time.

## Conclusions

With all of the information and feedback you have gathered, you can start to draw conclusions about how effectively you are providing feeds and meals overall. You can then identify problem areas and find ways to deal with these. For example, if you are not giving a vegan child a sufficient variety of food:

- research new meals and snacks to try
- carry out this research online and at the library, as well as asking the child's parents for tips.

### Assignment practice

The OCR model assignment will ask you to provide:

| Mark band 1 | Mark band 2 | Mark band 3 |
|---|---|---|
| **Brief** explanation of the suitability of each piece of equipment chosen considering three factors. | **Sound** explanation of the suitability of each piece of equipment chosen considering three factors. | **Comprehensive** explanation of the suitability of each piece of equipment chosen considering three factors. |
| **Basic** evaluation to include why equipment is selected. **No** rejections considered. | **Sound** evaluation to include why equipment is selected and others are rejected. | **Comprehensive** evaluation to include why equipment is selected and others are rejected. |

### Top tips

Command words:

- Brief – work includes a small number of relevant facts or concepts but lacks detail, contextualisation or examples.
- Sound – valid, logical, shows the student has secured most of the relevant understanding, but points or performance are not fully developed. Applies understanding and skills to produce the wanted or intended result in a way that would be useable.
- Comprehensive – the work produced is complete and includes everything required to show depth and breadth of understanding. Applies the understanding and skills needed to successfully produce the wanted or intended result in a way that would be fully fit-for-purpose.
- Basic – work includes the minimum required. It is a starting point but is simplistic and not developed. Understanding and skills are applied in a way that partly achieves the wanted or intended result, but it would not be useable without further input or work.

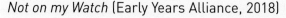

### Read about it

*Healthy Snacks, Happy Children* (National Day Nurseries Association, 2015)

*Not on my Watch* (Early Years Alliance, 2018)

*Nutritional Guidance for the Under Fives* (Early Years Alliance, 2017)

Stimpson, Jo, *The Children's Book of Healthy Eating* (Star Rewards – Life Skills for Kids, 2016)

# Unit R059

# Understand the development of a child from one to five years

## Topic areas

In this unit you will learn about:

1 Physical, intellectual and social developmental norms from one to five years
2 Stages and types of play and how play benefits development
3 Observe the development of a child aged one to five years
4 Plan and evaluate play activities for a child aged one to five years for a chosen area of development

## About this unit

In this unit you will learn about children's physical, intellectual and social development, and children's play. You will also learn about how to carry out observations of children's development, and how to provide good play activities to promote their development.

**How will I be assessed?**

You will complete a set assignment that contains two practical tasks. This will be assessed by your Centre and moderated later by OCR.

## Topic area 1 Physical, intellectual and social developmental norms from one to five years

Developmental norms tell us approximately when a child is likely to achieve certain developmental milestones, such as learning to crawl, learning to read and learning to communicate. Understanding developmental norms is very important, because it enables you to provide appropriate activities and support for children throughout their early years.

In this unit, you will learn about development norms from one to five years – covering physical development, intellectual development and social development.

### Getting started

How many important developmental milestones did you go through as a child?

- Make a list of the developmental milestones from one to five that you went through.
- Now take three different coloured pens. Underline all the **physical development** milestones in one colour, all the **intellectual development** milestones in another colour and all the **social development** milestones in a third colour.

### Key terms

**Physical development**
The development of gross motor skills (large movements) and fine motor skills (small, delicate movements).

**Intellectual development**
The development of the way the child's brain processes information received from surroundings and other people.

**Social development**
The development of the ways in which children experience and learn to handle their own emotions and relationships with others.

## 1.1 The expected development norms from one to five years

### Development is holistic

Once you understand the developmental norms, you will have insight into the child's learning and new skills. You will also be aware of what they are likely to learn next. This will inform your activity planning, and help you to provide activities that are appropriate for that child.

Understanding developmental norms also enables you to monitor a child's development and to notice if it is not in line with the expected developmental norms. This is important because a child may need outside support with an aspect of their development, and if so, it is beneficial for them to receive this support as soon as possible.

However, it is crucial to understand that children develop at different rates, and that the norms are just an approximate guide.

- Children will not all reach the same milestone at exactly the same time.
- It is to be expected that some children will reach the milestones a bit later than the norms specified in some developmental areas. Yet the same child may well be ahead in others.
- For example, a child may learn to walk and run early, but start to read comparatively late.

In this unit, you will learn about the developmental norms for children's:

- physical development
- intellectual development
- social development.

## Sequence of development

Children tend to develop in broadly the same sequence (or order). So even though the time at which they meet developmental norms might be different, they still tend to learn to stand before they walk and walk before they run.

However, there are still some exceptions. For example, a child with a disability may be expected to develop differently in some areas.

**Figure 3.1** Children develop in broadly the same sequence

## Physical development

Physical development is the term we use to refer to how children gain physical control of the movements made with their bodies. These movements fall into two categories:

- **gross motor skills**
- **fine motor skills**.

### Gross motor skills

The word 'gross' means large. Gross motor skills are the large movements made by the whole body, such as walking, jumping and balancing. Children develop many of these skills very quickly between one and five years of age.

Learning to walk involves mastering a series of gross motor skills.

- Usually a child will learn to pull themselves up to a standing position.
- They will go on to learn to walk with both hands held by an adult, then with one hand held.
- Finally, they will learn to walk alone.

### Fine motor skills

Fine motor skills are the small, delicate, manipulative movements made by the fingers. There are links between the development of fine motor skills and the development of vision. We call this **hand–eye co-ordination**.

A good example of this can be seen when children are threading cotton reels onto a piece of string. They need to:

- look to see where the hole is, then
- position the string in the right place in order to manipulate it through the hole.

You use hand–eye co-ordination in the same way whenever you thread a needle – and that can be very tricky sometimes.

Hand–eye co-ordination is also needed to achieve simpler fine motor tasks, such as seeing where an object is and picking it up.

Table 3.1 shows the expected physical developmental norms from one to five years of age. Study it carefully.

**Figure 3.2** Balancing is a gross motor skill

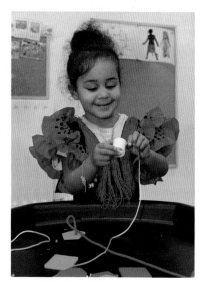

**Figure 3.3** Threading beads requires hand–eye co-ordination

**Table 3.1** Physical developmental chart. Can you think of activities or resources that would be good for promoting development at each of these stages?

| Approximate age of child | Aspect of physical development | |
|---|---|---|
| | Gross motor skills | Fine motor skills |
| 12 months | Sits down from standing position.<br>Stands alone briefly and may walk a few steps alone.<br>Throws toys intentionally. | Clasps hands together.<br>Uses sophisticated pincer grasp and releases hold intentionally.<br>Feeds self with a spoon and finger foods. |
| 15 months | Walks independently.<br>Crawls upstairs. Crawls downstairs feet first.<br>Sits in a child sized chair independently. | Tries to turn the pages of a book.<br>Makes a tower of two blocks.<br>Makes marks with crayons.<br>Holds own cup to drink. |
| 18 months | Walks confidently and attempts to run.<br>Walks up and down stairs with hand held by adult.<br>Bends from the waist without falling forwards.<br>Balances in the squat position.<br>Pushes and pulls wheeled toys.<br>Propels ride on toys with legs.<br>Rolls and throws balls, attempts to kick them. | Uses delicate pincer grasp to thread cotton reels.<br>Makes a tower of three blocks.<br>Makes big scribbles with crayons.<br>Can use door handles. |
| 2 years | Runs confidently.<br>Climbs low apparatus.<br>Walks up and down stairs alone, holding a handrail.<br>Rides large wheeled toys (without pedals).<br>Kicks stationary balls. | Makes a tower of six blocks.<br>Joins and separates interlocking toys.<br>Draws circles, lines and dots with a pencil.<br>Puts on shoes. |
| 3 years | Walks and runs on tip-toes.<br>Walks up and down stairs confidently.<br>Rides large wheeled toys using pedals and steering.<br>Kicks moving balls forward.<br>Enjoys climbing and sliding on small apparatus. | Makes a tower of nine blocks.<br>Turns the pages of a book reliably.<br>Draws a face with a pencil, using the preferred hand.<br>Attempts to write letters.<br>Puts on and removes coat.<br>Fastens large, easy zips. |
| 4 years | Changes direction while running.<br>Walks in a straight line successfully.<br>Confidently climbs and slides on apparatus.<br>Hops safely.<br>Can bounce and catch balls, and take aim. | Makes a tower of ten blocks.<br>Learning to fasten buttons and zips.<br>Learning to use children's scissors and cuts out basic shapes.<br>Draws people with heads, bodies and limbs.<br>Writes names and letters in play – begins to develop awareness that print carries meaning. |
| 5 years | Co-ordination increases.<br>Controls a ball well. Plays ball games with rules.<br>Rides a bike with stabilisers.<br>Balance is good, uses low stilts confidently.<br>Sense of rhythm has developed.<br>Enjoys dance and movement activities. | Controls mark making materials well (e.g. pencils, felt-tip pens).<br>Writing is more legible. Writes letters and short familiar words.<br>Learns to sew with children's sewing materials. |

## Intellectual development

Intellectual development is the term we use to describe the way the brain processes the information children constantly receive from their surroundings and other people. It is an important area of a child's development. Table 3.2 shows aspects included within the area of intellectual development.

### Language

Language is part of intellectual development. In order to communicate, children need to:

- listen and understand the communication from other people.
- understand what they want to communicate themselves.

Communication, therefore, relies heavily on thinking skills. (See the section on communication for more information on body language, listening and talking.)

Once communication is learnt, it actually helps children's thinking processes. You may sometimes find yourself 'thinking aloud', or in other words, talking out loud to yourself. People often do this unintentionally when they are problem solving or thinking creatively.

As you'll see in Table 3.2, language development is rapid in the early years, as children steadily progress from making vocalisations (sounds) all the way to talking in full sentences.

### Reading and writing

Together, the skills of reading and writing are known as **literacy**.

Children start to develop their literacy skills in the early years, when they begin to recognise and write letters of the alphabet and show an interest in books.

However, there are wide variations:

- Some children experience difficulty learning to read and write.
- They may continue to struggle with this throughout their education and beyond.

Children with strong **language** skills tend to become more confident readers and writers. So it is important that we give young children lots of varied language opportunities.

## Key terms

**Literacy** The ability to read and write (young children will be developing this ability).

**Language** An intellectual development skill that requires children to understand the communications of others, and what they want to communicate themselves.

**Figure 3.4** Children start to develop literacy skills in the early years

## Good practice

You can support young children's future literacy by helping them to enjoy books and stories, which increases their motivation to read. You can boost this motivation by using appropriate electronic devices. For example, you can:

- share text messages and emails from loved ones with children, who are usually very keen to find out what has been said
- interest children in appropriate online activities and games that require an element of reading, such as quizzes
- provide lots of mark making activities such as painting and drawing, as these help to develop the skills needed to write.

## *Communication*

**Communication** covers the way in which children master speech and other methods of communicating with others. This includes:

- body language – this is when physical behaviour expresses feelings. It includes body posture and movement, touch, facial expressions such as smiling, eye movement and the use of space (e.g. if a child chooses to stand away from someone).
- listening – listening is just as important as talking. Without listening, conversations are often ineffective. The ability to listen is connected to a child's **attention span**.

**Key terms**

**Communication** The giving and receiving of information.

**Attention span** The amount of time for which a child can concentrate on a particular activity.

- verbal – talking and other sounds – young children learn vocabulary at a very rapid rate, which enables them to talk with increasing sophistication. Other sounds such as crying, laughing, shrieking and groaning also communicate how a child is feeling.

- gesture – it is common for children and adults to gesture without being aware that they are doing so, as it is an ingrained part of behaviour. Children also gesture intentionally when they do not have the words to communicate what they want. For example, they may point to their favourite toy, if it is out of reach.

- sign language – children who are deaf or have a hearing impairment may learn to communicate in sign language. Children with learning difficulties that impact on their communication skills may learn a simplified sign language called Makaton.

- reading and writing – reading and writing are extremely important communication skills. Children who struggle to read and write can be at a disadvantage throughout education and beyond. Therefore, practitioners must provide plenty of opportunities to promote the learning and development of literacy skills.

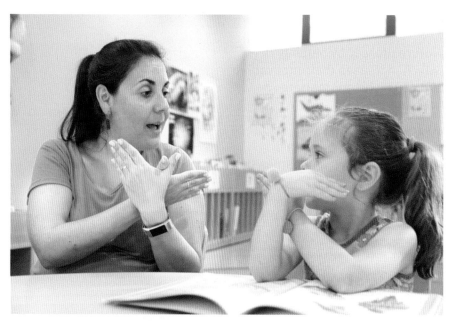

**Figure 3.5** Sign language may be used for communication

## Number skills

The development of number skills is closely related to the development of problem solving and reasoning skills. Together, these skills are often referred to as **numeracy**.

> **Key term**
>
> **Numeracy** The ability to recognise, understand and work with numbers (young children will be developing this ability).

There are many aspects to the development of numeracy, including:

- saying and using numbers
- counting
- recognising numbers
- using mathematical ideas to solve problems (e.g. sharing out toy cars fairly)
- recognising and drawing shapes
- recognising and making patterns
- using vocabulary relating to adding and subtracting (e.g. saying 'take one away', or 'add one more')
- beginning to do simple calculations, such as adding one or taking one away
- using language such as 'more', 'less', 'heavier' or 'lighter' when making comparisons.

## Good practice

In the early years, children need lots of opportunities to develop number skills through opportunities, such as number games and simple counting activities.

Practitioners sometimes use teaching devices known as 'number lines' or 'magic number squares' to help children with number skills. These are lines or square grids that feature numbers in ascending order. Children can touch the numbers to help them to do simple number operations such as adding and subtracting.

Beyond the early years, children can eventually progress to mathematic puzzles, which involve working out a number sequence using specially designed magic number squares.

## Activity

1 Using these weblinks, browse the range of number lines and magic number squares available:

www.hope-education.co.uk/search?phrase=number+lines

www.sparklebox.co.uk/maths/counting/100-squares.html#.
V9fTtg1TF2t

www.puzzles-to-print.com/number-puzzles/magic-square-worksheets.shtml

2 Which of the magic number squares do you think are suitable for children under five years of age?

3 Which of the magic number squares do you think are suitable for children over the age of five?

Table 3.2 below shows the expected intellectual developmental norms from one to five years of age. Study it carefully.

**Table 3.2** Intellectual developmental norms from one to five years. Can you think of activities or resources that would be good for promoting development at each of these stages?

| Approximate age of child | Aspect of intellectual development |
|---|---|
| 12 months | Looks for objects that fall out of sight, understanding that they still exist but cannot be seen. Memory develops. Remembering a past event enables anticipation of future events (e.g. may show excitement when placed in highchair for lunch). Begins to anticipate what comes next in the daily routine (e.g. a bath before bed). Increasingly understands basic messages communicated by family members. Can respond to basic instructions. Babbling sounds increasingly sound like speech, leading to first single words being spoken. Shows understanding that particular words are associated with people and objects by using a few single words in context. |
| 15 months | Will put away/look for familiar objects in the right place. Uses toys for their purpose (e.g. puts a doll in pram). Shows a keener interest in the activities of peers. Understands the concepts of labels such as 'you', 'me', 'mine' and 'yours'. Use of single words increases and more words are learned. |
| 18 months | Uses trial and error in exploration. Understands a great deal of what carers say. More words continue to be spoken and learned. Begins to use other people's names. |
| 2 years | Completes simple jigsaw puzzles (or 'play-trays'). Understands that actions have consequences. Builds towers of bricks. Will often name objects on sight (e.g. may point and say 'dog' or 'chair'). Vocabulary increases. Joins two words together (e.g. 'shoes on' or 'all gone'). Short sentences used by 30 months, with some words used incorrectly (e.g. 'I goed in' rather than 'I went in'). |
| 3 years | Child is enquiring. Frequently asks 'what' and 'why' questions. Uses language for thinking and reporting. Can name colours. Enjoys stories and rhyme. Vocabulary increasing quickly. Use of plurals, pronouns, adjectives, possessives and tenses. Longer sentences used. By 43 months, most language is used correctly. Can match and sort into simple sets (e.g. by colour). Counts to 10 by rote. Can count out 3 or 4 objects. Beginning to recognise own written name. Creativity is used in imaginary and creative play. |

**Table 3.2** Intellectual developmental norms from one to five years. Can you think of activities or resources that would be good for promoting development at each of these stages? (continued)

| Approximate age of child | Aspect of intellectual development |
|---|---|
| 4 years | Completes puzzles of 12 pieces. |
| | Memory develops, recalls many songs and stories. |
| | Attention span increases. |
| | Fantasy and reality may be confused. |
| | Imagination and creativity increases. |
| | Problem solves ('I wonder what will happen if ...') and makes hypotheses ('I think this will happen if ...'). |
| | Sorts objects into more complex sets. |
| | Number correspondence (counting out) improves. |
| | Begins to do simple number operations. |
| | Uses language more fluently. |
| | As understanding of language increases, so does enjoyment of rhymes, stories and nonsense. |
| | Speech is clear and understood by those who do not know the child. |
| | Begins to recognise more written words, and begins to be interested in books and electronic devices. |
| | Writes own name and copies other words and letters. |
| 5 years | Opinions and knowledge of subjects are shared using language for thinking. |
| | Vocabulary is also still growing fast. |
| | Enjoyment of books and electronic devices increases further as they learn to read. |
| | Spends longer periods engaged in activities and shows perseverance. |
| | Learns from new experiences at school. |
| | Learning style preferences may become apparent. |

**Figure 3.6** You can promote number skills through rhymes and games

## Social development

Social development considers the ways in which children experience and learn to handle their own emotions.

The relationships children have with others and the way they relate to them also comes under this area of development. This includes the attachments (or bonds) that children make with the key people in their lives, including their parents, carers and other close family members.

### Communicating with others

Communication – talking and conversations – is closely linked with the intellectual development of language and communication that you read about earlier.

Communicating is at the heart of:

- the relationships you have with the people who are most important in your life
- your daily interactions with all the other people that you meet.

In many ways, your ability to communicate affects the quality of your relationships and interactions. The same is true for young children, who crave closeness and affection from those who care for them (both parents and carers).

So it's important always to allow a child the time they need to say something. It can take a while for them to form their thoughts and speak at the same time. Try to work out what a younger child may be trying to say to you through body language or sounds – you can help them to feel heard by vocalising (saying) this. For example, if at meal time a child points at their cup and whines, you might say, 'Would you like your drink? Here you are.'

Talking and conversations with play mates and friends are increasingly important too as social development progresses.

### Acceptable behaviour

The way in which children handle their emotions gives rise to their behaviour. For example, when a child experiences frustration at not being able to do something, they might cry, throw something or show aggression. Children gain more control of their emotions as they develop, and this has an impact on their behaviour.

Toddlers are a good example:

- When a child is unable to indicate that they need help or want something specific, they may become frustrated and exhibit unacceptable behaviour.
- As their language and communication skills develop, they will learn to handle their frustration by asking for help, and this will enable them to behave in a socially acceptable way.

Manners also develop alongside language. A large part of politeness for young children is connected with using terms such as 'please', 'thank you' and 'sorry'. Usually they want to receive approval from others, and so want to behave in socially acceptable ways.

### Sharing

Sharing can be difficult for young children. For example, it can be very hard for them not to be able to play with a toy they want straight away because another child has it.

- They may well experience frustration and jealousy in this situation.
- This is because sharing involves something called 'delayed gratification' – having to wait for something that will bring them pleasure or satisfaction.
- The same applies when children must wait their turn in a game.
- The opposite side of the coin can be just as tricky – a child may be quite happily engaged in play when an adult takes an item away from them to give to another child because it is 'their turn'. This can also cause frustration and jealousy.

Children who don't have siblings at home can find sharing a particularly hard thing to get used to when they first start attending a group setting such as nursery. Staff typically find that they need to support children who are having difficulty sharing several times each day.

### Case study

Anna works in an early years setting. She sees two children – Max and Ava – arguing over a water wheel at the water tray. She approaches and asks if they have a problem. Ava says, 'I want it!' and tries to pull the toy away from Max. He says, 'I need it!'

Anna asks if either of them has already had a turn with it. Ava says she has, but then Chelsea played with it. Now it's her turn to have it back.

Anna says, 'Max hasn't had a turn yet, so we'll let him play with it first. And after five minutes, you can have another go, Ava. Does that sound fair?' Both children nod and Ava lets go of the water wheel.

As Max starts to play with it, Anna says, 'Ah, so you have got the bucket, Ava. How many yoghurt pots of water does it take to fill it up?'

1 Do you think Anna handled the situation well? Why is this?
2 Why do you think Anna asked Ava the question about the yoghurt pots and the bucket?

### Good practice

You always need to be aware of the fact that children will look up to you, and that you have a duty to be a positive role model whenever you are with them. This means behaving in socially acceptable ways yourself, and demonstrating good manners.

- You must not lose your temper and raise your voice. If you do, young children can be expected to display similar behaviour towards you or others sooner or later. (You would also be likely to frighten a child, which is also unacceptable behaviour.)
- Never use language that would be inappropriate for a child to repeat.

## Independence/self-esteem

Children gradually become more able to do things independently as they develop. Each time this happens, children are likely to feel proud and clever – especially when we praise them. This has a positive impact on their **self-esteem**, which in turn gives them **self-confidence**.

For young children, everyday routines that promote independence are valuable, particularly when it comes to gradually learning how to care for their own bodies. For example, you can:

- encourage a child to help with washing and dressing themselves
- praise a child for their attempts at self-care, such as brushing their own hair
- encourage children to take care of their environment, by asking them to help with the tidying up.

As children's sense of independence grows, they will want to make more choices for themselves, so it's important to promote this when you interact with them. For example:

- Invite children to choose which fruit to have at snack time.
- Give them a choice of different play activities both indoors and outdoors.

Leaving a parent's or carer's side to explore the environment demonstrates independence. You will learn more about this when looking at stages of play in section 2.1.

Encouraging a child to explore independently helps to prepare them for the stages of play. Practitioners will draw on their experience to assess how best to encourage a child. They will respond to the child's level of confidence, taking care not to overwhelm them.

For example, after saying hello, some children may need a practitioner to play close beside them right next to their parent/carer at first, perhaps by building a tower with blocks or making something with interlocking bricks. They may then slowly start to join in with the practitioner. As the child becomes more comfortable with them, another activity may be offered, such as sitting with the practitioner to make a puzzle together, or going with the practitioner to see something of interest nearby – the nursery pet perhaps.

However, a child who is feeling more confident may be happy to go and join the other children for story time, with the practitioner by their side, or perhaps try some tempting messy play.

Practitioners often ask a child's favourite activity in advance of the meeting, so they can offer the child something familiar to do that the child will enjoy.

### Key terms

**Self-esteem** When a child has a sense of self-worth or personal value.

**Self-confidence** When a child has a feeling of belief and trust in their own ability.

## Activity

Think back to the first time in your own life that you were able to do something significant independently. Most of us cannot remember much about our early years, so this can be an example from your more recent life – perhaps you can remember the first time you were allowed into town with just your friends, or the first time you used public transport alone?

Write a paragraph about how you felt. Include details about the impact the event had on your self-esteem and self-confidence.

## Good practice

Children need to be provided with opportunities to experience increasing independence in line with their needs, abilities and stage of development, in order to keep them safe.

Table 3.3 shows the expected social developmental norms from one to five years of age. Study it carefully.

**Table 3.3** Social developmental chart. Can you think of activities or resources that would be good for promoting development at each of these stages?

| Approximate age of child | Aspect of social development |
| --- | --- |
| 12 months | The sense of self-identity increases, as self-esteem and self-confidence develop. |
| | Waves goodbye (when prompted at first, and then spontaneously). |
| | Content to play alone or alongside other children for increasing periods of time. |
| 15 months | Curious – wants to explore the world more than ever, as long as carers are nearby. |
| | May show signs of separation anxiety (e.g. upset when left at nursery). |
| | May 'show off' to entertain carers. |
| | Can be jealous of attention/toys given to another child. |
| | Emotions can change suddenly – quickly alternates between wanting to do things alone and being happy to be dependent on carers. |
| | May respond with anger when told off or thwarted (e.g. may throw toys or have a tantrum). |
| | Can be distracted from inappropriate behaviour. |
| | Possessive of toys and carers – reluctant to share. |
| | Child 'is busy' or 'into everything'. |
| 18 months | Has a better understanding of being an individual. |
| | Very curious and more confident to explore. |
| | Becomes frustrated easily if incapable of doing something. |
| | Follows carers, keen to join in with their activities. |
| | Plays alongside peers (not interacting with them) and may imitate them |
| | Still very changeable emotionally. |
| | May show sympathy for others (e.g. putting arm around a crying child). |
| | Can be restless and very determined, quickly growing irritated or angry. |
| | May assert will strongly, showing angry defiance to adults. |
| | Can still be distracted from inappropriate behaviour. |

**Table 3.3** Social developmental chart. Can you think of activities or resources that would be good for promoting development at each of these stages? (continued)

| Approximate age of child | Aspect of social development |
|---|---|
| 2 years | Begins to understand own feelings. |
| | Identifies happy and sad faces. |
| | Experiences a range of changeable feelings that are expressed in various behaviours. |
| | More responsive to the feelings of others. |
| | Often responds to carers lovingly and may initiate a loving gesture (e.g. a cuddle). |
| | Peals of laughter and sounds of excitement are common for some. |
| | May use growing language to protest verbally. |
| | May get angry with peers and lash out on occasion (e.g. pushing and even biting them). |
| 3 years | Can tell adults how they are feeling. |
| | Empathises with the feelings of others. |
| | Uses the toilet independently and washes own hands. |
| | Can put on clothes. |
| | Imaginary and creative play is enjoyed. |
| | Enjoys the company of peers and making friends. |
| | Wants adult approval. |
| | Is affected by the mood of carers/peers. |
| | Less rebellious. Less likely to physically express anger because words can be used. |
| 4 years | May be confident socially. |
| | Self-esteem is apparent. |
| | Aware of gender roles if exposed to them. |
| | Friendships with peers are increasingly valued. |
| | Enjoys playing with groups of children. |
| | Control over emotion increases. |
| | Can wait to have needs met by carers. |
| | As imagination increases, child may become fearful (e.g. of the dark or monsters). |
| | Learning to negotiate and get along with others through experimenting with behaviour. |
| | Some considerate, caring behaviour shown to others. |
| | Experiences being in/out of control, feeling power, having quarrels with peers. |
| | Distracting the child works less often, but they increasingly understand reasoning. |
| | Co-operative behaviour is shown. |
| | Responds well to praise for behaviour, encouragement and responsibility. |
| 5 years | Starting school may be unsettling. |
| | Enjoys group play and co-operative activities. |
| | Increasingly understands rules of social conduct and rules of games, but may have difficulty accepting losing. |
| | Increasing sense of own personality and gender. |
| | Keen to 'fit in' with others – approval from adults and peers desired. |
| | Friends are important and many are made at school. |
| | Many children will have new experiences out of school (e.g. play clubs, friends coming for tea). |
| | Increasingly independent, undertaking most of their own physical care needs. |
| | May seek attention, 'showing off' in front of peers. |
| | Often responds to the 'time out' method of managing behaviour. |

**Figure 3.7** Children with good levels of self-esteem are more likely to feel happy

## Stretch activity

Understand the physical, intellectual and social development norms from one to five years.

1 Find a partner to work with.
2 Imagine that you work at a toddler group, and you have been asked to give a presentation to parents on child development from one to five years of age.
3 Choose one area of development to focus on – physical development, intellectual development or social development.
4 Prepare a presentation consisting of slides and notes. (The notes should consist of what you would say.)

## Test your knowledge

1 What does the term 'gross motor skills' mean?
2 Language is an example of a type of intellectual development. Give two further examples of types of intellectual development.
3 At what age would you expect a child to begin walking?

## Topic area 2 Stages and types of play and how play benefits development

**Synoptic link**

This topic area links with R057 Topic area 3, specifically section 3.3: The developmental needs of children from birth to five years.

### Getting started

Think back to when you were a young child.

Thought storm the ways in which you liked to play. You can include activities such as dancing or playing hide and seek. You can also include playing with favourite toys, such as dolls or a train set.

- Use a coloured pen and underline all of the activities and toys that you played with alone. This type of play is known as **solitary play**.
- In a different coloured pen, underline all of the activities and toys that you played with alongside other children. This is known as **co-operative play**.
- If there are some activities or toys that you played with both solitarily and co-operatively, underline them in both colours.

**Key terms**

**Solitary play** When a child plays alone.

**Co-operative play** When children play together, actively working towards a common goal.

**Parallel play** When children play alongside one another but do not play together.

**Associative play** When children communicate and play with the same type of toy or activity.

## 2.1 The stages of play

To develop well, children need to learn and understand many things, and they learn best through play.

Children love to play and they engage in play naturally – they don't need to be told to do it. If toys, resources or traditional activities aren't available to them, children will find ways to play with whatever is at hand, or they will create their own activities. The four stages of play include solitary play, **parallel play**, **associative play** and co-operative play.

In this section, you will learn about the four stages of play:

1 solitary play
2 parallel play
3 associative play
4 co-operative play.

Children play differently at each stage. Let's look at each in turn, considering what happens at each stage of play and the expected ages for each stage.

### Solitary play

All children, whatever their age, will frequently engage in solitary play, or playing on their own. At times this is probably because friends to play with are not available, but often it is their choice. When playing alone, children can set their own pace and explore their own thoughts or ideas. They may also concentrate for longer periods.

Solitary play is the first type of play that babies and young children experience. Until the age of around two years, children only play alone. During this time, they are discovering aspects of themselves and their environment.

Activities that promote solitary play include:

- imaginary play (e.g. role play, small world play)
- puzzles
- books
- video/computer games
- mark making (e.g. drawing, painting and writing)
- construction play (e.g. blocks and interlocking bricks).

## Parallel play

From around two to three years of age, children will enjoy playing alongside one another at the same activity – in parallel with each other. They remain engrossed in their own activity, even though they might:

- change their activities to match others (e.g. if the child next to them at the play dough table starts to roll out dough with a rolling pin, they may do the same thing)
- share resources.

They will not actually interact or play directly with another child. Children have companionship, but even in the middle of a group of children, remain independent in their play.

Activities that promote parallel play include:

- playing with dough
- making things
- complete a puzzle
- painting.

**Figure 3.8** Solitary play is the first type of play that babies and young children experience

**Figure 3.9** In parallel play, children may do the same thing and even share resources, but they remain engrossed in their own activity

## Associative play

This stage generally occurs from between the ages of three and four.

During associative play, children communicate (talk to each other) and play with the same type of toy or activity. The situation is generally unstructured (see the examples below). But each child has their own idea of what they want to do – this is known as their 'play agenda'.

The children don't co-ordinate their play objectives or interests. This means there will be some trouble! Conflicts arise at this stage when children have separate ideas that others do not share. Children especially have trouble when trying to play imaginatively together.

Activities that promote associative play include:

- riding a bicycle alongside another child
- games with few rules, such as rolling a ball back and forth
- building with bricks alongside each other
- playing at the sand tray
- water play.

**Figure 3.10** In associative play, children communicate and play with the same type of toy but each child has their own 'play agenda'

## Co-operative play

From around four to five years of age, children begin to play co-operatively. This occurs when they fully interact and communicate, playing with others and working towards a common specific goal. They can use rules and organise themselves into roles, such as 'You be the doctor and I'll be the patient'.

Activities that promote co-operative play include:

- imaginary role play (may include props such as dressing-up clothes, imaginary areas such as a home corner, or toys such as teddies or tea sets)
- board games (e.g. Lotto, snakes and ladders)

### Activity

Try to arrange a visit to a playgroup (ensuring you have gained permission from your teacher and the childcare setting).

1. Watch children of different ages playing. Can you spot examples of solitary play and co-operative play?
2. Make a note of what children are doing while engaged in this play.
3. In your next lesson discuss the types of play you observed with a partner.

- playground games (e.g. 'What's the time, Mr Wolf?', 'Traffic lights')
- construction activities
- circle games (e.g. 'Here we go round the mulberry bush', 'The farmer's in his den')
- partner dancing.

**Figure 3.11** In co-operative play, children fully interact and communicate. They can use rules and play games together

Although ages are suggested for each stage of development, you'll find that you can observe older children playing in the ways described for younger children. Once children achieve a stage of development, they will still at times play in the ways they have before. For example:

- All children like to have their personal space and play alone sometimes. Most children will also stand back and watch others without joining in at times, especially in new circumstances.
- Older children will be seen playing alongside each other with little interaction when engaged in an art or craft activity, such as drawing or making jewellery.

## 2.2 Types of play

Children initiate play instinctively or on impulse because they find it enjoyable, exciting and fun. To a certain extent, the way in which children play is influenced by the activities and play resources they have available. But children can find ways to play virtually anywhere and with anything. You may have seen children finding ways to play in the supermarket or when waiting for a bus.

Children enjoy and learn from different types of play in very different ways. By understanding these, parents and carers can provide a broad range of play activities to ensure that a child's development is well rounded.

---

**Test your knowledge**

1 Explain what happens at the solitary play stage.
2 At what age are children usually at the parallel play stage?
3 Name four activities that promote associative play.
4 Explain what happens at the co-operative play stage.

## Manipulative play

**Manipulative play** occurs when children engage in an activity that involves making delicate operating movements with their hands and fingers. Learning and practising these fine movements is part of a child's physical development.

- At first, a young child's manipulative movements are crude – young babies use their whole hand to pick up and hold objects such as rattles. Using the whole hand in this way is known as a 'palmar grip'.
- In time, they will be able to pick up smaller toys and objects using just their index finger and thumb. This is known as a 'pincer grip'. Many skills that children will use throughout their lives depend on manipulative skills – for example, writing and using tools.

Manipulative movements are linked to the development of vision. Children need to look carefully at the object they want to manipulate, then move their fingers accordingly – using hand–eye co-ordination. A good example is when a child fastens buttons or a zip.

Activities that promote manipulative play include:

- mark making, such as drawing, painting, writing and chalking
- malleable materials – materials that can be squeezed and shaped (e.g. clay, play dough, cornflour paste, jelly and modelling clay)
- craft activities (e.g. collage, making recycled models, making things from paper or card, such as planes or hats)
- construction toys (e.g. blocks, interlocking bricks and popping beads)
- activities that require tools such as scissors, a computer mouse, utensils and cutlery.

**Figure 3.12** Mark making promotes manipulative development

### *Puzzles, drawing and painting*

Puzzles, drawing and painting are good examples of activities that require manipulative skills. Puzzle pieces need to be carefully manipulated in order for them to fit together. Children's drawings and paintings will become increasingly sophisticated as their manipulative skills improve.

**Activity**

Browse a supplier of children's art and craft materials. You could do this in a shop, online or by looking at a catalogue. Make a list of the art and craft tools available that would require children to use their manipulative skills. (Only include those suitable for children aged three to five years of age.)

## Co-operative play

Co-operative play begins from the time children are around three years of age. It occurs when two or more children play together, interacting with one another, with shared goals in mind.

A child who is playing co-operatively will be interested in the children they are playing with, as well as the activity they are doing.

**Good practice**

Young children need plenty of support when playing co-operatively.

At times they will need adults to help them manage problems or conflicts that arise, due to difficult issues such as sharing, patience, give and take, or handling emotions when they lose a game.

Through these experiences and lots of practice, children increasingly learn to successfully play co-operatively with others.

Activities that promote co-operative play are shown on pages 146–147.

### *Board games*

Board games and circle games (such as 'Here we go round the mulberry bush') are a very good example of co-operative play, especially when children are required to follow rules essential to playing well together, such as taking turns.

Pair or group imaginary games also require co-operative play, and might involve children organising themselves into roles, for example: 'You work in the shop, and I will be the customer.'

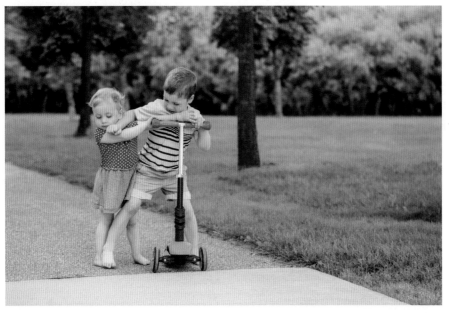

**Figure 3.13** Young children need plenty of support when playing co-operatively. At times they will need adults to help them manage conflicts

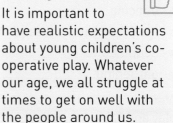

**Good practice**

It is important to have realistic expectations about young children's co-operative play. Whatever our age, we all struggle at times to get on well with the people around us.

## Imaginative play

Imaginative play is an important way in which children learn and make sense of the world. It occurs when a child acts out an experience they have had in their play, or when they pretend to be having an experience that interests them. This allows them to explore various roles in life.

Activities that promote imaginative play:

- role play (may include props such as dressing-up clothes, imaginary areas such as a home corner, or toys such as teddies or tea sets. Older children may enjoy simple acting/drama)
- play with small world toys (e.g. cars and a road play mat, a farmyard set, toy figures, a doll's house)
- story boards, story bags, puppets.

## Physical play

We have looked at manipulative play, which is an aspect of **physical play**. In addition, physical play also includes activities that:

- require children to use their gross motor skills – the movements they make with their arms, legs, feet or their entire bodies
- develop balance and/or co-ordination
- develop the **senses**
- exercise the body and limbs (promoting fitness).

In order to thrive, young children need a balance between physical play opportunities and more restful activities. Many children's settings, such as nurseries and pre-schools, now allow children to move freely between indoors and outdoors during many of their play sessions. This helps children to choose when they wish to use lots of space to play physically, such as to run or ride a tricycle.

Activities that promote physical play include:

- ball games (e.g. involving kicking, throwing, catching, bouncing)
- different ways of travelling (e.g. running, jumping, skipping, hopping, rolling, crawling, climbing)
- playground equipment (e.g. slides, swings, climbing frames)
- push and pull toys
- stepping stones
- mini trampolines
- dancing
- feely bag games (based on touch)
- sound Lotto
- gardening.

Also see the section above for activities that promote manipulative play and Table 3.4 on pages 158–156. for activities and resources that promote children's physical development.

**Figure 3.14** Imaginative play with small world resources. What other small world resources do you think this child would enjoy?

## Key terms

**Physical play** Activities in which children use their manipulative or gross motor skills, develop balance or co-ordination, develop the senses or exercise the body and limbs (promoting fitness).

**Senses** Sight, smell, hearing, taste and touch.

## *Ball games, ride on toys and climbing*

Ball games, ride on toys and climbing are good examples of simple activities that children will start to engage in when they are very young. As they grow up, their play in these areas will become more sophisticated and may carry on into adulthood.

Ball games promote many physical skills, such as kicking, throwing, catching and bouncing balls. In later years, children will learn how to use the skills to participate in sports and team games.

Toddlers begin playing on ride on toys by using their feet to push along on the ground. They progress onto tricycles with pedals, then bikes with stabilisers, and finally they ride a bike without stabilisers. Ride on toys also include scooters, space hoppers and, for older children, skateboards.

As well as promoting climbing skills, climbing helps children to develop strength and fitness. It is important to allow a young child's climbing skills to develop at their own pace. Some children may feel a little anxious at first when leaving ground level, for example, to climb the ladder of a low nursery slide. But they soon progress to climbing cubes, then more challenging climbing frames. Older children may climb trees, climbing walls or go rock climbing.

## Creative play

Children are engaged in **creative play** when they express themselves by responding to something that sparks their imagination. For example, a child might engage in model making by making something with materials or objects, such as:

- art and craft resources
- household items (such as cereal boxes or blankets)
- natural objects (such as leaves or twigs).

A child might also express themselves in other ways, such as:

- dancing
- singing
- making music
- making up a story.

Young children are often more interested in the process of their creative play than in the end product. They may enjoy making something very much, but not want to keep it.

You may hear any end products created by children referred to as 'artefacts'. For example, when a childcare setting keeps some examples of children's drawing, painting and craft activities in a file so they can keep a record of the progress they make in their creative development over time, they may call this the child's 'artefact file'. The term tends to be used just for end products that can be kept. So a sandcastle made by a child is unlikely to be called an artefact.

> **Key term**
>
> **Creative play** When children express themselves by creatively responding to something that sparks their imagination.

> **Key term**
>
> **Artefact** An end product of children's creativity that can be kept, such as a drawing, painting or model.

### Good practice

Sometimes, the end product of a child's creative play may not be recognisable, but it is very important to praise their handiwork. Disapproving or making fun of a child's efforts can have a negative effect on their self-esteem and well-being. It might also discourage them from engaging in creative play, which could eventually impact on their development.

Activities that promote creative play:

- music
- dance
- mark making (e.g. painting, drawing, printing)
- collage
- making models (e.g. with recycled objects or malleable materials)
- sand play
- water play
- exploring nature (e.g. playing with leaves, collecting conkers, looking at shells)
- stories
- imaginary play.

### Music and dancing

Making music is a wonderfully creative play experience. Children can express themselves by playing musical instruments. They can also respond creatively to the music that they hear – by dancing along, for example, in their own unique way.

### Stories

When children listen to a story they are immersed in a rich creative world. The characters come alive in children's minds and they are often thinking hard – and creatively – about what might happen next as the story unfolds. Children enjoy hearing favourite stories over and over again, because it allows them to keep revisiting and developing the world they have imagined. Children also love to look at books themselves, enjoying the pictures and the stories these conjure up long before they can read.

Story bags or boxes can extend this experience by promoting creative play. These containers are filled with items that relate to a particular story. For instance, in a bag containing the book *The Tiger Who Came to Tea*, children might find a tea set, play food, toy tigers and figures to represent the other characters in the story. Children can play with these freely, acting out an aspect of the original story, making up their own, or perhaps doing something completely different. For example they may be inspired to make a zoo enclosure for tigers out of interlocking bricks.

**Case study**

Ali works in an early years setting. He is approached by three-year-old Marlie. She is holding out a model she has made from recycled objects, including yoghurt pots and cardboard boxes. To Ali, it looks like a tower. Marlie says, 'Look at this! It's the donkey I saw on the beach ... I don't know what his name was.' Ali replies, 'So it is! Well done, Marlie. Perhaps we could think up a name for him. Have you got any ideas?'

1 Do you think Ali's response was positive? Explain your reasons.
2 If Ali had said, 'I could not tell it was a donkey,' how might Marlie have felt?

**Activity**

1 List as many specific examples of types of play as you can.
2 Now look back over section 2.2 to see if you have missed some. If so, add them to your list.

For more activities that promote play, development and skills, see Table 3.4.

## 2.3 How play benefits development

Children benefit hugely from play. It allows them to:

- develop and learn
- relax
- have fun
- be active.

Let's look at the developmental and learning benefits of play in more detail. These fall into four main categories: physical, intellectual, social and creative.

### Physical development

Physical benefits of play include the development of:

- fine manipulative skills
- gross motor skills
- balance and co-ordination
- fitness and strength.

#### Hand–eye co-ordination

Physical play helps children to develop hand–eye co-ordination. As children become more experienced in manipulating the objects they see, their hand–eye co-ordination becomes more sophisticated. For example, a pre-school child will thread large beads onto string, but in their primary school years, they will be able to thread a needle.

#### Increase fitness

Physical activity promotes fitness. This is vital to children's health and well-being. Young children are built to be physically active and enjoy the opportunity to run around and move freely. Being fit and active also helps children to avoid becoming overweight.

For examples of activities that promote physical development, see Table 3.4.

**Figure 3.15** Climbing is a key physical skill for children to develop. Do you think that climbing successfully impacts on children's self-confidence?

## Intellectual development

The intellectual benefits of play fall into three categories:

- mental stimulation
- problem solving
- communication.

### *Mental stimulation*

Children can have new ideas and thoughts and explore them during play. They can also:

- make their own discoveries
- learn about the world
- learn to understand concepts such as counting
- develop awareness of mental processes, such as reading.

When high quality play activities are provided, children's attention span and their memory will both develop.

### *Problem solving*

Through play, children can experiment and test things out. For example:

- A child playing at a water tray might discover which objects sink and which float.
- Through trial and error, a child might work out the best way to stick two items together, or to transport many objects from one place to another.

This makes learning a real and vivid experience.

**Figure 3.16** Through play, children can work things out

### *Communication*

Play strongly promotes children's communication and language skills, especially when children spend time in a language-rich environment. This is a place (at home, or at a childcare setting perhaps), where adults and peers talk frequently with a child. They will expose them to songs, rhymes, stories and new vocabulary.

Children can also be encouraged to:

- ask questions
- listen
- follow instructions during play activities
- talk about their own experiences and ideas.

Remember that some young children will be learning more than one language through their play.

For examples of activities that promote intellectual development, see Table 3.4.

## Social skills

Play is vital to well-being – children need it to thrive and to feel happy. Play can impact positively on children in several ways.

### Independence

When children go off to play with their peers, they are independent of their parent or carer (even if they are supervising from across the room). This is a big step for a young child.

A playgroup will be many children's first experience of being cared for by someone other than a close family member.

Play also helps children to master skills that foster independence. For example, dressing-up and dressing dolls help children to learn to dress themselves.

### Confidence

Successfully trying new activities and becoming increasingly independent helps children to build confidence.

- Many play activities specifically foster confidence – such as games that involve talking in a group, or the act of joining in with singing and dancing.

**Figure 3.17** Learning to ride a bike can boost confidence

- Activities that involve appropriate risk-taking can also boost a child's confidence, such as learning to ride a bike or putting their face in the water at a swimming pool.

## Sharing

To behave in a socially acceptable way, children need to learn how to share. This is not an easy task, because it requires a child to put what is fair, or another person's feelings, above what they want themselves.

In group settings, practitioners tend to spend quite a lot of time helping children to cope with sharing, and supporting them to resolve disagreements over objects desired by more than one child.

Working together on a project or activity helps to foster children's sharing skills. For example, several children might create a painting together outside on a large roll of paper spread out on the floor.

## Self-esteem

When children have positive play experiences in which their contributions, ideas and feelings are respected, there is a positive effect on their self-esteem.

When a child feels good about themselves, they are likely to approach play enthusiastically, and this will influence how much they benefit from activities. Playing with both friends and adults helps children to feel accepted, loved and valued.

## Communication skills

Play promotes conversation and non-verbal communication between children, and between children and adults. Generally, children soon learn to put across their own ideas, and to understand other people's ideas – this is the basis for all shared play.

Resources such as play phones and walkie-talkies can promote communication during play. (Also see Intellectual development, above.)

Play also promotes social skills such as:

- taking turns
- learning to follow the rules – this includes rules that relate to socially acceptable behaviour (such as using good manners and respecting other people) and rules that relate to safety (such as no running up the slide or no jumping from the climbing frame)
- learning to get along with others.

For examples of activities that promote social skills, see Table 3.4.

## Creative skills

Play has a wonderful way of promoting creativity. When children can play freely with access to a wide range of resources, creativity will naturally occur.

### Activity

Talk to the parent of a child aged around three or four years. Ask them to tell you about the development of their child's social skills.

- How does the child cope with sharing, taking turns, following the rules and getting along with others?
- How has the parent supported their child's development of social skills?

## Imagination

Children use their imagination effectively when:

- they think and behave imaginatively – this includes problem solving, mark making, crafts or imaginary play
- their imaginative activity is purposeful – their play fulfils an objective. For example, making a tall tower that does not fall down, or getting from one side of the room to the other without touching the floor
- they express creativity in a unique way, creating something original – for example, a child may create a picture, a model, or their own song or dance.

## Problem solving and creative thought

In this context, 'creative thought' refers to the process of children using imaginative thinking and problem solving ability to resolve issues for themselves.

To support children in developing these skills, you can encourage 'divergent thinking'. Divergent thinking is the name given to the thought processes used to generate creative ideas by exploring many possible solutions. You might use this method yourself in your own life. For example, if you are asked to help plan a theme or event for children such as 'Under the sea' or 'the Olympics', you might start by thought storming possible related ideas.

You can encourage children to develop imaginative thinking and problem solving skills by providing them with a play environment with lots of different types of resources and materials. This could include a play environment within a forest school setting, with natural materials such as sticks and leaves. It's important then to allow children to make connections between these by 'mixing up' resources, such as:

- allowing a child to put bricks in the water tray to make a 'mermaid's home'
- allowing cars on the play dough table so a child can drive them along roads they have made.

You can encourage problem solving and creative thought during play by asking children questions such as:

- 'What do you think we should we do?'
- 'What can we try?'
- 'How could we?'

You can also plan activities that encourage children to suggest ideas and solve problems for themselves, such as a game in which children can access a range of resources in order to cross the room without stepping directly on the floor.

For examples of activities that promote creative skills, see Table 3.4.

**Activity**

1 Explain what the term 'benefits of play' means in practice.
2 Think of one type of play and explain some of the ways in which children benefit from it. The more detail you can include, the better.

**Table 3.4** Activities and resources that promote children's development/skills.

| Area of development/skills | Resources | Activities |
|---|---|---|
| Physical development | For **fine** motor skills:<br>Tools – scissors, brushes, rolling pins, cutters.<br>Computer mouse.<br>Threading beads.<br>Modelling clay/cornflour paste/play dough/jelly.<br>Dressing-up clothes with buttons to fasten.<br>For **gross** motor skills:<br>Different-sized balls, hoops and quoits.<br>Large wheeled toys including ride on toys such as tricycles to promote balance and co-ordination.<br>Tunnels and parachutes.<br>Carts to push and pull.<br>Low stilts.<br>Skittles, hoopla, bats.<br>Slide, climbing frame, balance beam, swing, stepping stones. | Playground games (e.g. 'What's the time, Mr Wolf?', 'Traffic lights') for movement such as creeping, running.<br>Negotiating a chalk-drawn 'road' for awareness of space.<br>Obstacle course for travelling around, under, over and through.<br>Pretending to go 'on a bear hunt' for moving with confidence and imagination. |
| Intellectual development | Counting beads, sorting toys, scales, weights.<br>Rulers, height chart.<br>Number lines/cards, magnetic numbers and letters, shape sorters, puzzles.<br>Construction resources of different shapes.<br>Clocks.<br>Play money.<br>Varied range of mark making materials (pencils, felt tips, paint etc.).<br>Letter frieze (e.g. letter line or poster) and alphabet line.<br>Books, comfortable book area, talking books and computers.<br>Musical recordings.<br>Signs and labels. | Counting how many they need (cups, for example), sharing out for calculating.<br>Singing number songs and rhymes.<br>Tidying up for sorting objects/positioning (e.g. 'That goes on the shelf next to the bricks').<br>Cooking for recognising ingredients, weighing and following instructions.<br>Completing puzzles for developing problem solving skills.<br>Story time.<br>Retelling stories with props for understanding.<br>Feely bags to promote descriptive language.<br>Role play.<br>Rhymes, songs, poems.<br>Mark making opportunities in role play areas for starting to 'write' shopping lists in their play. |
| Social skills | Puppets, dolls and soft toys (with expressions, for exploring feelings).<br>Table-top games (e.g. Lotto, snakes and ladders).<br>Dressing-up clothes.<br>Range of dolls/figures showing representation of people in the world (in terms of ethnicity, age, gender, disability).<br>Well-equipped imaginary areas including a home corner and comfortable quiet area for resting and talking, cultural artefacts (e.g. representing food and cooking from around the world in the home corner resources). | New activities to build confidence, excitement and motivation to participate and learn (e.g. leaves in the water tray or earth to dig instead of sand).<br>Games for rules and turn-taking.<br>Celebrating festivals for awareness and respect of the wider world.<br>Pouring drinks and putting on clothes for independence.<br>Circle time for talking about home. |

**Table 3.4** Activities and resources that promote children's development/skills. (continued)

| Area of development/skills | Resources | Activities |
|---|---|---|
| Creative skills | Wide range of art and craft resources including different colours and textures (e.g. paper, card, tissue, cellophane, paint, glue, felt tips, crayons, craft feathers, lollipop sticks, sequins, buttons, pipe cleaners).<br>Musical recordings and musical instruments.<br>Equipped role play areas.<br>Dolls. | Wide range of art, drawing and craft activities (e.g. painting outside with water and large brushes for expression and imagination).<br>Making textured collages.<br>Music and movement.<br>Music time with dancing/singing/playing instruments.<br>Puzzles for problem solving.<br>Child-led activities that encourage creative thought and problem solving (e.g. how to cross the room without stepping on the floor using a range of resources). |
| Remember: Children play and develop holistically. All of these resources and activities can be used in many ways to promote different aspects of development and skills, even at the same time. | | |

Also see section 2.1 for further examples of activities that promote development/skills.

---

## Test your knowledge

1 Discuss how play benefits children in terms of mental stimulation.
2 Name a social skill that is a benefit of play. Discuss the impact that this skill may have on a child's relationships with others.

---

**Topic area 3** Observe the development of a child aged one to five years

• • • • • • • • • • • • • • • • • • • • • • • • • • • • • • • • • • • • • • • • • • • • • • •

### Getting started

Practitioners regularly spend dedicated time observing each child in their care. Working with a partner, thought storm reasons why this might be done.

## 3.1 Observation and recording

**Observation** is the term used to describe the process of a practitioner watching and recording a child's behaviour (the things that they do and say).

### Reasons for carrying out observations

Over time, these observations help you to build a picture of a child's individual development and behaviour. This picture helps you to track a child's progress, and to plan activities that will support and extend their learning and development in each area.

It also helps practitioners to spot when a child's development is not consistent with the expected development norms – you will learn more about this in the section on how to use observation findings, starting on page 166.

### Methods of observation

Methods of observation include:

- narrative
- checklist
- snapshot
- time sample
- participative
- non-participative.

You'll learn about the different methods of observation below. We'll look at:

- what each method of observation involves
- when each method would be appropriate
- how the observation would be recorded.

As you'll see, it's important to think about the type of information you need to collect and why you want the information when selecting which method of observation to use.

#### Narrative observation

Narrative observation is when a child's natural spontaneous behaviour is observed for a set period of time. During this time, other adults in the room will not lead or prompt the child, but they will respond if the child approaches them. This means that the child will most likely be engaged in a child-led activity, such as any type of freely chosen play. They might change activities and move around the environment during the observation.

During this type of observation, the practitioner:

- carefully watches the activity of the child
- writes down everything they see and hear the child do and say, including facial expressions and gestures
- records how other children and adults interact with the child, including their speech.

**Key term**
**Observation** The process of watching and recording a child's behaviour to assess and track their learning and development.

**Good practice**
Early years settings are required to keep development records for every child. Generally, each child will have their own file. During their time at the setting, it will be filled with observation records, and records of their activities. This will include some of the child's own work.

This way of recording is often called a 'naturalistic observation'. Writing everything down is difficult to keep up, so this type of observation is only done for a short length of time – often less than five minutes.

Alternatively, a practitioner may record everything they see, but at timed intervals. For example, they may observe the child for three minutes every hour throughout a half-day play session. This variation on the narrative observation is often called a 'running record'.

When capturing a narrative observation, it's important to only write down what you see, and to remain non-judgemental. For instance, if the target child tells someone else to 'go away', you would write exactly that, rather than saying the child 'was being rude and showing off'.

| NARRATIVE OBSERVATION | Name of child: Amina |
|---|---|
| Completed by: Charlotte Preston | Date: 18/1/22    Time: 11.05    Duration: 3 mins
Location: Outside play area |

Amina sees the paint rolling activity set up. She walks towards it, stands still and looks. She takes an apron from the coat peg. Puts it on, fiddles with Velcro fastening then leaves it undone.

She crouches down, takes a roller and dabs it in the yellow paint tray. She blobs it onto the paper. She laughs and points to the yellow splodge it makes. She rolls the roller up and back a few times, then across, smiling. Stands and holds the roller up, calls to nearby adult, "Look, look, Claire. It's yellow." Claire approaches smiling. "It's like sunshine, isn't it? Shall I help you with that apron?" Amina turns around and backs towards Claire and she fastens it at the back.

Figure 3.18 Narrative observation example

## Checklist

In this method of observation, a form reminds the observer to look for particular skills or reflexes that the child has. The observer ticks these off as they are seen and records the date.

This method is often used for:

- assessing a child's stage of development and collecting baseline information when a child first starts attending a setting
- observing babies and toddlers, whose physical development will typically progress rapidly.

The observations may be done over time or children may be asked to carry out specific activities, such as building a tower of bricks.

| Activity | Yes | No | Date | Observer's comments |
|---|---|---|---|---|
| Runs confidently | | | | |
| Climbs low apparatus | | | | |
| Rides large wheeled toys without pedals | | | | |

**Figure 3.19** Checklist observation example

## Snapshot observation

This type of observation is when a practitioner notices a child doing something interesting and spontaneously observes them very briefly, often just for a minute or two.

A practitioner may begin to observe a child on seeing them:

- show a new skill
- play in a particular way that they have been hoping to capture.

Snapshot notes are often made on sticky notes. On many occasions, these can be added to a child's file just as they are, making this method quick and efficient. Practitioners often say that snapshot observations build over time to document 'the learner's journey'.

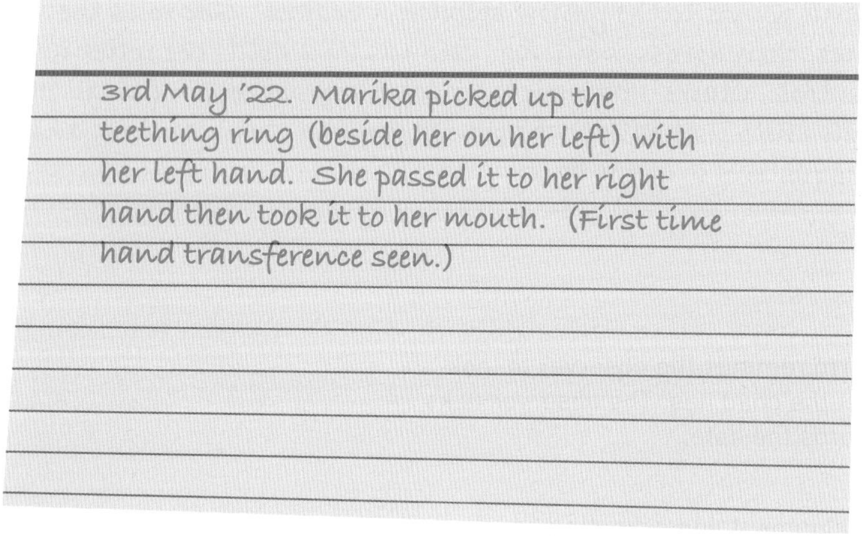

> 3rd May '22. Marika picked up the teething ring (beside her on her left) with her left hand. She passed it to her right hand then took it to her mouth. (First time hand transference seen.)

**Figure 3.20** Snapshot observation example

## Time sample

The observer decides on a period of time for the observation, perhaps two hours or the length of a session. The child's activity is recorded on a form at set intervals – perhaps every 10 or 15 minutes. This tracks the child's activity over the period of time.

However, significant behaviours may occur between the set time periods, and these will not be recorded.

*10.00am*

*Armani is sitting at the painting table next to Demetrius. She picks up her paintbrush and looks at him. He looks back. She smiles and holds her brush out to him. Demetrius takes it and smiles back. Armani says 'Thank you.' Demetrius says 'Thank you.'*

*10.15am*

*Armani gets down from the table. She goes to a practitioner. Armani hold up her hands and says, 'Paint! Look! Wash hands.'*

**Figure 3.21** Time sample example

## Participative observation

This occurs when the observer deliberately interacts with the child during the observation.

- The practitioner might ask the child to do certain things to see if they can manage particular milestone tasks, such as building a tower of blocks, or completing a puzzle. This information might then be recorded on a checklist form (see the example in Figure 3.19).
- Alternatively, a practitioner might ask a child questions to check their understanding (e.g. 'What happened then?') or for insight into their actions ('Why did you do that?').

## Non-participative observation

This occurs when the observer does not interact with the child at all. This gives an authentic picture of the child's natural behaviour.

The practitioner will settle in a spot where they can see the child well without the child realising they are being observed. This makes recording an observation easier, as there is no need for the practitioner to write down their own speech or actions.

This method has drawbacks:

- It can be difficult to find a spot that is close enough to allow you to hear everything without giving yourself away.
- There is a chance that the child will wander off to another part of the setting, and they may not play in a way that demonstrates the skills or behaviour you want to record.

The narrative observation method is a popular recording choice for the non-participative observer.

## Activity

Carry out an initial observation to meet the child you will study and to inform the choice and planning of activities. Try to arrange to spend time with a child under the age of five, so that you can plan some activities to promote your chosen developmental area. This can be:

- a child in your family
- a child you meet as the result of arranging a visit to a group or organisation (e.g. a toddler group, pre-school or nursery)
- a child that comes into lessons for observation purposes
- a child that is known to you and their parents have agreed you can observe.

During your time with the child, carry out a narrative observation. Think carefully about how this can inform the choice of activities that you will plan for them.

## Methods of recording

Once a method of observation has been chosen, a practitioner will plan how to record the observation.

### Charts

Filling in a chart can be a very user-friendly way of recording a lot of information quickly and effectively during a period of observation.

### Written methods

Some observations will be written out in full, with the practitioner noting as much detail as possible. See Figure 3.18 for an example.

### Examples of a child's work

Some of the work children produce – such as art and craft items, their drawings and their early writing – can be kept as an excellent, accurate record of what they did during an activity. These work samples (or artefacts) can be kept in a child's development file. Some items may be displayed within the setting for a short time first.

Practitioners should provide written explanations alongside the examples of work, sharing an understanding of what the child has achieved/how they have met the developmental norms.

### Photographs

Photographs are an excellent way of recording a snapshot of a child engaged in an activity. For example, a photo of a child smiling with friends at the top of a climbing frame could capture confidence (social development) and the level of their gross motor skills (physical development).

## Good practice

Practitioners regularly meet a child's parents or carers to share their observations and development records. This helps everyone to work in partnership together, which is the best way to support and care for the child.

When a practitioner first meets a child, observation is a good way to get to know them. Learning about a child's preferences and character will help practitioners to:

- establish a good rapport (relationship) with the child
- plan appropriate activities.

The better a practitioner knows a child, the more effective their planning.

Photos are also a good way to keep a record of an end product created by a child that cannot be kept, such as a house a child has built with blocks or even a snowman. Video recordings can also be used in a similar way.

## Good practice

Photos, video recordings and any sort of observation must never be made without the written permission of a child's parents or carers. When you make a recording, it must only be used for the purpose intended, and must not be passed on to others.

- Full-face photos of the child must not be submitted – they should be taken from the side or blanked out.
- Personal information, such as full names and addresses, should not be used.
- If you work in an organisational setting (such as a nursery), you must also have the written permission of that setting before taking photos or video.

For this qualification, large numbers of photos are not expected or required.

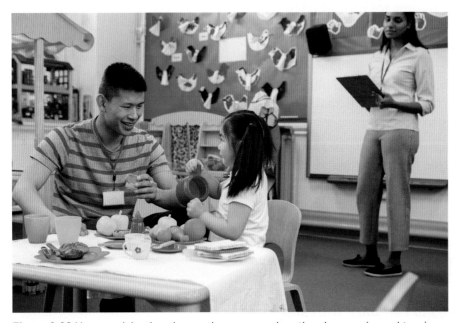

**Figure 3.22** Non-participative observation occurs when the observer is unobtrusive and does not interact with the child at all

## Confidentiality and permission

The guardians of children (usually their parents) have the right to decide what information is collected, recorded and stored about them. Practitioners **must** obtain **written permission** from parents authorising them to carry out observations and keep documentation on record. This must be signed and dated.

The details of observations should be kept confidential unless withholding information would affect the well-being of the child. So it's important that you handle and store assessment documents and notes in line with a setting's confidentiality policy.

- It's essential that you gain permission from workplace supervisors **before** carrying out observations.
- Supervisors will probably ask to see your completed observation, and the child's family may also want a copy.
- You must also protect the child's identity by changing their name, or using another way of identifying them, e.g. 'target child' or 'Child A' or 'Child 1'.

## How to use observation findings

As a practitioner, you will use the information you have gathered during observations to track a child's progress. You can undertake this by drawing conclusions from what you have seen. For example, if you observe a child using a knife and fork well, you may conclude that they are able to use some tools independently.

### Comparing a child with expected developmental norms

After observing a child, you can then compare their development with the expected developmental norms for a child of that age, within the developmental area.

This will enable you to spot when development is not consistent with the expected norms. This is important because the child may need extra support, such as more opportunities to participate in activities that will help them to develop a particular skill.

Sometimes, practitioners will notice that the difference between a child's development and the expected developmental norms presents cause for concern. They are often the first to spot when a child has a specific individual need, such as a communication difficulty.

In this case, they will follow their setting's procedures for discussing the matter with parents or carers. They are likely to recommend that the parents access outside support from a professional such as a doctor or health visitor.

### How to use observation findings to compare with stages of play

In a similar way, you can also compare the play you have seen a child exhibit (engage in) with the stages of play expected at specific ages. You will then be able to see where play is not consistent with the expected norms.

1 solitary play – all ages, but the only stage of play until around the age of two years

2 parallel play – from around two to three years of age

3 associative play – develops between the ages of three and four

4 co-operative play – from around four to five years of age.

If a child isn't engaging in the play stage expected for their age (e.g. if an older child only engages in solitary play), this indicates that they may need extra support, or that there is cause for concern.

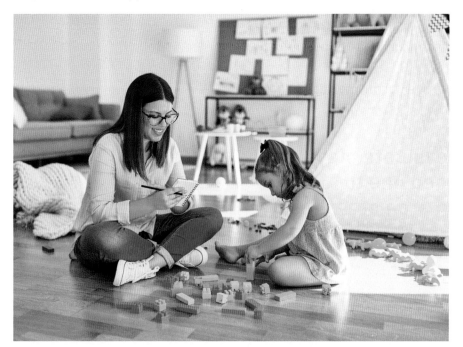

**Figure 3.23** Participative observation occurs when the observer deliberately interacts with the child during the observation

## *How to use observation findings to compare with types of play*

Comparing observation findings with types of play may reveal inconsistencies in the types of play children access.

Sometimes, a child might have little interest in playing in particular ways, which can impact on their learning and skill development. For instance, a child may choose to play outside on apparatus and ride on toys as much as possible, and rarely visit role play areas.

Once you are aware of this, you can think of new ways to promote the activities to the child – see the following case study for an example.

## Case study

Nursery practitioner Nazneen has noticed that four-year-old Carmen loves to play outside on apparatus and ride on toys as much as possible. She rarely chooses to sit down in the art and craft area, or visit role play areas. Nazneen thinks about how to interest her in these things, and comes up with some new outdoor activities.

The next day, Nazneen suggests that all the ride on toys in the playground could be emergency vehicles today. Carmen is quick to make siren noises as she rides around. Nazneen brings out the dressing-up clothes, including a police uniform, fire-fighter's helmet and a doctor's uniform. When Carmen sees other children riding around dressed up, she joins in too.

● How else could Nazneen encourage Carmen to engage in role play?

## Topic area 4 Plan and evaluate play activities for a child aged one to five years for a chosen area of development

## Getting started

Imagine that you work in a pre-school. Three-year-old Dayne will be attending for the first time today. During their initial visit to the pre-school, Dayne's dad remarked that it will be good for him to try messy art and craft activities, because he has only experienced drawing at home.

Make a list of all the experiences and skills involved in messy art and craft activities that will be new to Dayne. For example, putting on an apron and using a glue stick.

## 4.1 Plan and evaluate play activities

It's important to provide fun, interesting activities that will give children the chance to learn new things and develop their skills. By providing a broad range of activities, you can promote children's learning and development in each of the developmental areas.

To do this successfully, you need to be well prepared. This involves thinking things through carefully in advance, then making written plans. In this section, you will learn how to plan a range of different activities for a chosen developmental area, and consider the following factors:

- chosen activity
- reason for choice
- aims
- developmental area
- timing
- safety considerations
- appropriate resources
- how the activity will be introduced to the child.

When planning, practitioners tend to think of activities to promote one area of development. But in reality, play activities often promote more than one area of development. For example, when a child learns to write their name, they are developing:

- physical fine motor skills needed to control a pencil well enough to form letters
- intellectual skills by learning to recognise and remember the letters that make up their name. This includes remembering the sequence of the letters.

> **Synoptic link**
>
> This topic area and section 4.1 in particular link with R057 Topic area 4, specifically section 4.3: How to ensure a child-friendly safe environment.

## Activity

1 Think back to when you were a young child. Write down your earliest memory of taking part in an organised activity, such as making a card at nursery, or playing a circle game at school.
2 Now thought storm the things you were likely to be learning during the activity. For example:
   - learning to use scissors more effectively
   - learning to write your name
   - learning how to take turns
   - learning how to cope emotionally with being out of a game.
3 Share your list with a partner. Together, decide which areas of development were promoted by the activity. For example:
   - learning to use scissors more effectively = physical development
   - learning to write your name = physical development and intellectual development
   - learning how to take turns = social development
   - learning how to cope emotionally with being out of a game = social development.

## How to plan for different play activities

There are numerous different play activities you can provide for children. There are well-loved traditional activities, for example, sharing nursery rhymes, as well as all the imaginative new things you might consider in a moment of inspiration – an imaginary game where children pretend they are a crayon being used by a giant, perhaps!

It's exciting to have so many activity options. But for their overall learning and development, children need a balanced programme of activities.

A good way of making sure that children receive this is to plan a number of activities to promote each developmental area in turn. By doing this, no important aspect of learning and development is left out.

There are several different ways of recording activity plans. Many early years settings such as nurseries and pre-schools design their own activity planning forms, which are charts for staff to fill in.

- They are often displayed so that staff can refer to them during the play session.
- They also allow parents to see what their child will be doing.

Information on how to plan for different play activities is provided in sections 1.1, 2.1, 2.2 and 2.3.

## What to include in a plan and reasons why

Now let's look at the points to consider when planning play activities to promote a chosen developmental area.

### *Aims*

This is the section of a written plan that shows the purpose of the activity, or in other words, how a child or group of children are expected to benefit from taking part. Plans should include one or more clearly stated aims per activity.

It is important to think carefully about your aims. When an activity is finished, it will be evaluated. The evaluation process involves considering how well the activity actually met the aims in practice. You will learn how to evaluate activities later in this section.

### *Developmental area*

In this part of the plan, the primary developmental area to be promoted is recorded.

**Good practice**

Planning play activities well helps promote each area of development thoroughly. It also allows you to provide activities that are well organised, safe and relevant for the children you look after. Happily, this will also increase the activities' fun factor.

## Chosen activity

This section of the plan is a brief description of the activity. It may help you to think of it as a clear, specific title for the activity.

From this line alone, other practitioners reading the plan should have a good impression of the activity to come. This is important, because in a busy group setting such as a nursery, staff need to be able to see what's happening that day at a glance.

## Reasons for choice

This section of the plan gives you a place to record the relevance of your activity in promoting the developmental area you have chosen/the benefits to the child. In other words, it is your chance to explain the link between your activity and the developmental area that it promotes.

You can use this section to explain why the activity is relevant to a particular child.

## Timing

This is basic information about how long it will take to prepare an activity, carry it out and clear away afterwards.

In a busy early years setting, a smooth-running routine is needed to ensure that everything happens when it should, including meal times, sleep times and outdoor play times. Events need to unfold like clockwork, without children feeling rushed or under pressure.

Therefore, practitioners need to know the time it takes to carry out certain tasks. This comes with experience, but it is a good idea to:

- double-check that you are being realistic about timing at the planning stage
- ask someone appropriate to look over your timings if you are unsure about them.

## Safety considerations

In Unit R058, you learnt about child safety, including how to keep play areas safe by carrying out a risk assessment. Using those skills, you should think carefully about any possible safety issues you will need to address before carrying out each activity that you plan. For example:

- Is the area to be used safe, whether inside and outside? (This may include risk assessing traffic, or whether any gates are safely closed.)
- Is there appropriate supervision available?
- Are the resources child-friendly (e.g. no sharp items and clean materials)?
- Is the environment/working area clean?

**Good practice**

Generally, new workers are most likely to underestimate the time it takes to complete tasks such as setting up an activity or clearing away. So take time to break down each task. For example:

- You might initially think that you will be able to set out paint and brushes in a minute or so. But if you have to mix the paint from powder first, it is going to take much longer.
- If paint is going to be used again later in the day, it will not take long to put the pots and brushes to one side. But, if they need to be washed up, dried and stored away, it will take much longer.

Once you have identified safety issues, you will need to plan the measures you will take to limit the risk to an acceptable level. This information must be recorded clearly on the plan.

**Figure 3.24** Allow plenty of time to set up activities

## Appropriate resources

The 'resource' section is the place to list all of the appropriate resources needed for an activity.

Remember to check that these will be available for use at the right time. If a setting has particularly expensive or large resources, such as a tablet or set of drums, these might be shared by several different classes or groups.

Also, check the arrangements with the person supervising you, especially if your activity requires:

- less common resources that they may not have (e.g. ready-made papier-mâché)
- a large quantity of the same item that might need collecting over time (e.g. several empty washing-up liquid bottles)
- fresh ingredients (e.g. for cooking activities or messy play)
- expensive resources (e.g. craft items such as decorative beads).

## How the activity will be introduced to the child

Children need to know what to do in order to engage with your activities. You will often need to outline or explain the activity when you first introduce it to them.

When it comes to planning the introduction, it helps to think about the individual child's experiences. You can do this by asking yourself a few key questions.

If you know the child well already (perhaps they are a family member), you may know many of the answers. But don't worry if you do not – you can simply ask the child's parents or carers. If you are visiting an early years setting (such as a crèche) to carry out your activities, you can ask a member of staff instead.

- Has the child taken part in this type of activity before?

   This information helps you to judge how much detail is needed when introducing your activity. This is important as a child may not feel confident to engage in a new type of activity if it is not fully explained to them.

   However, if a child has undertaken a similar activity before, over-explaining your activity can be off-putting. For example, making a collage with pasta will not need much explanation if the child has made collages with bottle tops and buttons in the recent past.

- Is the child familiar with the resources you will be using?

   Imagine that you plan to play a simple game of snakes and ladders with a child. If the child has previously played another board game involving a dice, they will be familiar with throwing a dice and will understand that the result of the dice throw is related to action on the board.

   But if their experience of board games is limited to Lotto, in which a dice is not used, they will need an introduction to the purpose of a dice and how to use it.

- Does the child have the skills needed to carry out any tasks required independently?

   This question helps you to plan the support a child is likely to need during an activity. For example, many pre-school children will need help with the task of cutting with scissors, even if they have taken part in lots of arts and craft activities. This is because the skill of using scissors is often not perfected until the end of the pre-school years.

## Good practice

Generally speaking, it is absolutely fine for children to need some support with a task during your activity. But if a child will need a lot of support throughout in order to be able to do the activity, have a careful think about whether it is appropriate for the child's age and stage of development by asking yourself the following questions:

- Have I selected an activity that is currently too advanced for the child?
- Could there be a way to simplify the activity?
- Can I plan something similar that is more appropriate? (For example, instead of making a model from clay, perhaps a child can make one from salt play dough, which will also set hard if left to dry out but is easier to manipulate.)

When you are planning activities for a group of children, think carefully about whether the activity is suitable for everyone. Some children may have an individual need that will make it difficult or impossible for them to participate. In this case, you should adapt the activity so that it is an **inclusive activity** (meaning that everyone can join in).

If this is not possible, plan a different activity that is suitable for everyone instead. This ensures equal opportunities for all.

## Case study

Gareth works at a crèche. He has been planning activities for Friday's play session, and has included a parachute game. His supervisor tells him that five-year-old Barney has just been booked in for the session. Barney is a wheelchair user, and will not be able to stand up to play parachute games alongside the others. This means that he will be too low to grasp the parachute when everyone else takes hold of it.

Gareth decides to adapt the game to make it inclusive. Instead of having the other players stand up for the game, he decides to have them kneel down. This way, they will be around the same height as Barney when he is sitting in his wheelchair, so they will all be able to hold the parachute and play the game together.

1 Do you think the solution is a good one? Support your answer with reasons.
2 What would Barney have thought about the activity if it had not been adapted?
3 How might the other children have felt if the activity had not been adapted?

### *Outline of activity*

This section of the example chart is for expanding on the type of activity, by recording what should happen and how. It often helps to imagine that you won't be carrying out the activity yourself and that instead you are writing clear instructions for a colleague. It may include information on how to set out the activity (see below).

### *Setting out activities*

Always give some thought to how you will present your activity, because this is a key part in its introduction to a child. An activity that is well set out will be more appealing, and this will affect how keen a child is to participate from the start. Activities will be most successful when a child feels drawn to them and cannot wait to get started.

Let's say that the planned activity is imaginary play in a home corner, for example:

- You could lay the kitchen table with a dinner set, and perhaps sit some teddies up to the table, seemingly ready to eat a meal.
- You could also put pots and pans on the play cooker, with play food inside.
- This is likely to entice children to play. It also gives them a play idea to follow up – making dinner for the waiting teddy family.

Alternatively, if your activity is to play with a train set:

- You could piece part of the track together on the floor and position some trains on it, before introducing the activity to a child.
- You could also place some spare pieces of track alongside. This is more attractive than just showing them a box containing pieces of track and trains.
- Children are likely to want to continue making the track so that they can push the trains around on a journey.

### Supporting activities

When carrying out activities, it is important to provide children with the level of supervision and support that they need. This is essential for keeping children safe and happy. Generally, more supervision is required for younger children or challenging activities.

In a group setting, children can play safely and independently during some activities as long as adults in the room are keeping a general eye on things, and are ready to step in if needed. The children can approach an adult if they need assistance or if they would like an adult to participate in their play.

However, some activities would not be safe for children without close one-to-one supervision from an adult. See Unit R058 for further safety information.

**Figure 3.25** Set up a home corner to draw children's interest

## Activities

Imagine that you are undertaking work experience in a crèche.

1 In the playroom, a small group of children aged three to five years are independently playing shops. A girl approaches you and asks if you need to buy anything. What do you think she wants you to do?
2 In the toddler room (for children aged one to two years), the staff have set up a paddling pool with shallow water. What level of child supervision do you think will be required? Give reasons for your answer.

## Stretch activity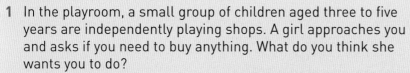

1 Decide which developmental area you would like to focus on. Choose from:
- physical development
- intellectual development
- social development.
2 Thought storm four activities that promote your chosen area. Write them down.
3 Now, select your favourite activity of the four. Write up your own activity plan for your favourite activity.

## How to use observation findings to inform choice of activity

Observation findings give us an overview of children's development and learning in each area of development. You can use this information along with your knowledge of the expected development norms to provide appropriate activities for children. This should include some activities that are appropriately challenging, so as well as thinking about what children can do now, you should consider what they are likely to learn next.

As you learnt in section 3.1, observation also enables practitioners to notice:

- when a child's development is not consistent with the expected norms
- when a child's play is not consistent with expected play stages
- how and how often children engage in different types of play.

By considering observation findings when planning activities, practitioners can make sure that they meet the needs of children who need extra support, such as:

- more opportunities to participate in activities that will help them to develop a particular skill
- encouragement to participate in particular activities
- support to enable them to participate or get the most out of an activity (such as one-to-one assistance).

4 Does the observation reveal evidence of the child not having achieved any of the expected development milestones? For example, did they have difficulty doing a task you might expect them to be able to do? Make notes of your findings.

5 Draw conclusions about the child's current developmental progress. Do they seem to be on track in this area of development?

## How to evaluate plans for play activities

Evaluating activities is the process of thinking about how effective your activities have been. You can identify what works well and what can be improved, so that you can provide higher quality activities. It also helps you to be as effective as possible in your role.

### *Using feedback from others and using self-reflection*

Throughout the evaluation process, you will be working towards answering this key question, 'How well did my activity meet my aims?'

There are two key methods which are best used together:

- feedback from others
- self-reflection.

An important part of evaluation is recalling the activity in your head. But before you start the evaluation process, it is useful to gather together some physical evidence to consider:

- Observations you made at the time.

  This can include written child observations and any activity reports you may have written. It can also include entries made in a reflective work diary or notebook.

- Feedback you were given by parents/carers, and/or other practitioners.

  This may have been given verbally, or a written feedback sheet on your activity may have been completed. (Perhaps you were required to get written feedback as evidence of your activity.)

- Evidence from children.

  For example, children might have given you verbal feedback on the activity, which you wrote down. Or perhaps their work products show evidence of how well the activity met their needs.

Once you have gathered your evidence together, start by looking through it all carefully to refresh your memory. Then you will be ready to start the first part of the evaluation process – identifying the strengths and weaknesses of the activity.

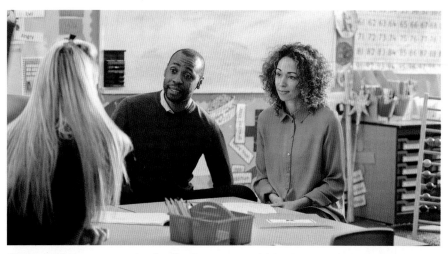

**Figure 3.26** You may receive feedback on your activities from other practitioners

## Successes, strengths and weaknesses

It is important for you to identify the successes, strengths and weaknesses of an activity. You need to reflect on how well you planned it and how successful it was or wasn't. This will help you improve the activity for the future.

## Changes or recommendations to improve activity and planning

Reviewing your activity and suggesting ways you could improve it next time, is a very positive part of the process, as you will start to see what you can do differently to make your activity the best that it can be. The improvements you recommend may be suggestions from others (such as parents or carers) and/or your own ideas.

## Draw conclusions – were the aims met?

The final task in the evaluation process is to sum up by drawing conclusions. One of the most effective ways of doing this is to answer this all-important summary question:

● Taking into consideration all of the strengths and weaknesses you identified, how effectively overall were the aims of the activity met?

You might also like to consider whether it is worth repeating the activity if you included the improvements suggested, or if, taking everything into consideration, it would be better to think of a new activity to meet the same aims.

Lastly, think about how you can apply the things you have learnt as a result of this activity when you plan other, different activities. The following case study gives an example.

**Good practice**

When evaluating, it is important to be honest about how the activity went, particularly if things did not go as well as you would have liked. Only then can you learn from your experiences.

**Test your knowledge** ✔

1 What is the purpose of evaluating activities?
2 How can feedback from others inform your evaluation of activities?

## Case study

Kyle plans an activity for music time. In his plan, he says that the musical instruments should be given out and then the person leading the activity should explain what the children are going to do.

Kyle's classmate reviews his plan and says that children would be distracted by looking at or fiddling with the musical instruments and would not want to stop and listen to the leader of the activity explaining what they had to do.

Kyle thinks about this and realises that it would be better to explain what the children had to do before they are given the musical instruments. Kyle thinks about this a bit more and realises that he can apply his learning to other plans too. For example, when planning a gardening activity, he can plan for the leader of the activity to explain what the children have to do before they give out the cuttings to each child to plant.

1 Do you think that Kyle's reflection on how to plan an activity will help to improve his gardening activity plan? Explain the reasons for your answer.

## Assignment practice

### The evidence you need to produce

- Complete at least one observation of a child between one to five years, choosing your own observation and recording method, and recording your own findings. You will also choose the developmental area on which to base your observation.
- Use your observation findings to plan a suitable play activity for the child you observed. The play activity must relate to the observation you have completed.
- Gather feedback on your planned play activity.
- Use the findings from feedback gathered, and self-refection, to complete your evaluations.

When creating this evidence, it may help to do the following:

- Think carefully about whether you should be a participative observer or a non-participative observer. This decision should complement the observation method you have chosen.
- Use your observation findings to plan a suitable play activity soon after completing your observation, while it is fresh in your mind.
- Consult parents/guardians/carers about possible improvements to the play activity.

## Read about it

### Reference books

Fawcett, Mary and Debbie Watson, *Learning Through Child Observation*, 3rd edition (Jessica Kingsley Publishers, 2016).

Meggitt, Carolyn, *Understand Child Development* (Teach Yourself, 2012).

Palaiologou, Ioanna, *Child Observation: A Guide for Students of Early Childhood*, 4th edition (Learning Matters, 2019).

### Weblinks

Advice from Teach Early Years:

www.teachearlyyears.com/nursery-management/view/making-observations

# Glossary

**Antenatal care** The care given to a pregnant mother and her unborn baby during pregnancy and ahead of the birth.

**Artefact** An end product of children's creativity that can be kept, such as a drawing, painting or model.

**Associative play** When children communicate and play with the same type of toy or activity.

**Attention span** The amount of time for which a child can concentrate on a particular activity.

**Barrier method** A method of contraception in which a device or preparation prevents sperm from reaching an egg.

**Birth partner** Someone who will attend antenatal classes and support the mother throughout pregnancy and the birth.

**Caesarean section** An operation in which a surgeon delivers a child by cutting through the wall of the mother's abdomen.

**Communication** The giving and receiving of information.

**Co-operative play** When children play together, actively working towards a common goal.

**Creative play** When children express themselves by creatively responding to something that sparks their imagination.

**Diagnostic test** Used to diagnose certain medical conditions in an unborn baby.

**Fertility** Being able to conceive children.

**Fine motor skills** The small, delicate, manipulative movements children make with their fingers.

**Gross motor skills** The large movements children make with their whole bodies.

**Hand–eye co-ordination** Using the vision system to control, guide and direct the hands to carry out a manipulative task.

**Hazard** A hazard is an item or situation that could cause harm to a child.

**Hormonal method** A method of contraception in which hormones prevent eggs from being released from the ovaries, thicken cervical mucus to prevent sperm from entering the uterus, and thin the lining of the uterus to prevent implantation.

**Inclusive activity** An activity in which everyone can join in, including disabled children or children with additional needs.

**Infertility** Not being able to conceive children after 12 months (or more) of regular unprotected sex.

**Intellectual development** The development of the way the child's brain processes information received from surroundings and other people.

**Language** An intellectual development skill that requires children to understand the communications of others, and what they want to communicate themselves.

**Literacy** The ability to read and write (young children will be developing this ability).

**Manipulative play** Physical play involving delicate, operational movements made with the fingers.

**Numeracy** The ability to recognise, understand and work with numbers (young children will be developing this ability).

**Nutrients** The nourishment that comes from the food we eat.

**Observation** The process of watching and recording a child's behaviour to assess and track their learning and development.

**Parallel play** When children play alongside one another but do not play together.

**Physical development** The development of gross motor skills (large movements) and fine motor skills (small, delicate movements).

**Physical play** Activities in which children use their manipulative or gross motor skills, develop balance or co-ordination, develop the senses or exercise the body and limbs (promoting fitness).

**Postnatal** After birth.

**Pre-eclampsia** A condition causing high BP in pregnancy and after labour. It must be monitored closely and can be serious if not treated.

**Risk** The likelihood of a hazard actually causing harm.

**Screening test** Identifies whether an unborn baby is more or less likely to have certain conditions at birth.

**Self-confidence** When a child has a feeling of belief and trust in their own ability.

**Self-esteem** When a child has a sense of self-worth or personal value.

**Senses** Sight, smell, hearing, taste and touch.

**Social development** The development of the ways in which children experience and learn to handle their own emotions and relationships with others.

**Solitary play** When a child plays alone.

**Transition** A process or a period of change from one state or condition to another, when young children usually need support, e.g. moving from a bed to a cot, starting to eat solid foods, starting pre-school, sleeping in their own bedroom.

**Transition stage** This links the end of the first stage of labour and the beginning of the second stage of labour.

**Weaning** The process of introducing babies to solid foods.

# Index

# Photo credits

**p.1** © Oksana Kuzmina/stock.adobe.com; **p.4** © Arcady/stock.adobe.com; **p.5** © Drobot Dean/stock.adobe.com; **p.7** © Watthana/stock.adobe.com; **p.9** © areeya_ann/stock.adobe.com; **p.10** © Miroslav/stock.adobe.com; **p.12** © ViDi Studio/stock.adobe.com; **p.18** © Samuel B./stock.adobe.com; **p.19** © Daniel Ernst/stock.adobe.com, **p.20** © Silas Stein/dpa/Alamy Live News; **p.21** © kzenon - 123RF; **p.25** © hedgehog94/stock.adobe.com; **p.27** © kzenon - 123RF; **p.28** *t* © Monkey Business/stock.adobe.com, *b* © Gilles Paire/stock.adobe.com; **p.31** *t* © Ermolaeva Olga/stock.adobe.com, *b* © Rafael Ben-Ari - 123RF; **p.34** © Angela Hampton Picture Library/Alamy Stock Photo; **p.35** © Tyler Olson/stock.adobe.com; **p.39** © arztsamui/stock.adobe.com; **p.41** *t* © UK City Images/Alamy Stock Photo, *b* © zlikovec/stock.adobe.com; **p.42** © Kzenon/stock.adobe.com; **p.43** © didesign/stock.adobe.com; **p.44** © Andrey Popov/stock.adobe.com; **p.46** © Jules Selmes/Hodder Education; **p.49** © Tomorrow's Child UK Ltd; **p.50** © yooranpark/stock.adobe.com; **p.52** © Jules Selmes/Hodder Education; **p.57** © Mediscan/Alamy Stock Photo; **p.58** © all_about_people/Shutterstock; **p.59** © Jules Selmes/Hodder Education; **p.60** © spotmatikphoto – Fotolia; **p.62** © Jules Selmes/Hodder Education; **p.63** © Andrew Callahan/Hodder Education; **p.67** *t-b* © British Standards Institute, © BHTA, © European Commission, © UK Government, © UK Government; **p.68** © John Gustafsson - Made by myself based on the specifications in EN 71-6:1994, **p.69** © British Standards Institute; **p.71** © Jules Selmes/Hodder Education; **p.73** © Suriyawut/stock.adobe.com; **p.76** © Maxx-Studio/Shutterstock.com; **p.78** © Jules Selmes/Hodder Education; **p.79** © Pond Thananat/Shutterstock.com; **p.83** © Daddy Cool/stock.adobe.com; **p.84** © krugloff – Shutterstock; **p.85** *l* © indigolotos – Shutterstock, *r* © Billion Photos – Shutterstock; **p.86** © Dumitru/stock.adobe.com; **p.89** *tl* © ACORN 1/Alamy Stock Photo, *br* © Africa Studio – Shutterstock; **p.90** *t* © Stockbyte/Getty Images/Child's Play SD113, *b* © Stockbyte/Getty Images/Child's Play SD113; **p.91** © Wilawan Khasawong - 123RF; **p.95** © Jules Selmes/Hodder Education; **p.100** Public Health England in association with the Welsh Government, Food Standards Scotland and the Food Standards Agency in Northern Ireland; **p.102** © mmg1design/stock.adobe.com; **p.103** © MIA Studio/stock.adobe.com; **p.104** © Daniel JÐdzura/stock.adobe.com; **p.105** © denys_kuvaiev/stock.adobe.com; **p.110** © kornnphoto/stock.adobe.com; **p.111** © Africa Studio/stock.adobe.com; **p.114** © Daisy Daisy/stock.adobe.com; **p.121** © Martina/stock.adobe.com; **p.122** © Jules Selmes/Hodder Education; **p.125** © Jules Selmes/Hodder Education; **p.127** © Jules Selmes/Hodder Education; **p.129** © Rawpixel.com/stock.adobe.com; **p.130** *t-b* © Jules Selmes/Hodder Education; **p.133** © yAOinLoVE/stock.adobe.com; **p.134** © JuanCi Studio/stock.adobe.com; **p.137** © Jules Selmes/Hodder Education; **p.143** © Jules Selmes/Hodder Education; **p.145** *tr* © yAOinLoVE/stock.adobe.com, *bl* © Oksana Kuzmina/stock.adobe.com; **p.146** © famveldman/123RF.com; **p.147** © Monkey Business/stock.adobe.com; **p.148** © Jules Selmes/Hodder Education; **p.149** © anoushkatoronto/stock.adobe.com; **p.150** © Jules Selmes/Hodder Education; **p.153** © Andrew Callahan/Hodder Education; **p.154** © Andrew Callahan/Hodder Education; **p.155** © phpetrunina14/stock.adobe.com; **p.165** © dglimages/stock.adobe.com; **p.167** © Krakenimages.com/stock.adobe.com; **p.172** © Jules Selmes/Hodder Education; **p.175** © Dumitru/stock.adobe.com; **p.178** © sturti/E+/Getty Images